BIG HITS

42 easy-to-play piano arrangements

Wise Publications
part of The Music Sales Group
London/New York/Paris/Sydney/Copenhagen/Berlin/Madrid/Tokyo

Published by
Wise Publications
14-15 Berners Street,
London W1T 3LJ, UK.

Exclusive Distributors:
Music Sales Limited
Distribution Centre, Newmarket Road,
Bury St Edmunds, Suffolk IP33 3YB, UK.
Music Sales Corporation
257 Park Avenue South,
New York, NY 10010, USA.
Music Sales Pty Limited
20 Resolution Drive, Caringbah,
NSW 2229, Australia.

Order No. AM997986
ISBN 978-1-84938-148-2

Editied by Jenni Wheeler.

Printed in the EU.

Your Guarantee of Quality
As publishers, we strive to produce every book to the highest commercial standards.
This book has been carefully designed to minimise awkward page turns and to make playing from it a real pleasure.
Particular care has been given to specifying acid-free, neutral-sized paper made from pulps which have not been elemental chlorine bleached.
This pulp is from farmed sustainable forests and was produced with special regard for the environment.
Throughout, the printing and binding have been planned to ensure a sturdy, attractive publication which should give years of enjoyment.
If your copy fails to meet our high standards, please inform us and we will gladly replace it.

www.musicsales.com

Contents

All You Need Is Love The Beatles 8

American Pie Madonna 4

The Bare Necessities (from *The Jungle Book*) 14

Beautiful Christina Aguilera 11

Big Spender (from *Sweet Charity*) 20

Big Sur The Thrills 16

Breaking Free (from *High School Musical*) 23

Candle In The Wind Elton John 26

Can't Help Falling In Love Elvis Presley 36

Clocks Coldplay 28

Crazy Patsy Cline 34

Day Tripper The Beatles 39

Don't Cry For Me Argentina (from *Evita*) 42

Every Little Thing She Does Is Magic The Police 44

God Only Knows The Beach Boys 48

Hallelujah Leonard Cohen 50

Heartbeat Buddy Holly 52

Hero Mariah Carey 54

Innocent Eyes Delta Goodrem 56

The Lady In Red Chris De Burgh 61

A Little Time Beautiful South 64

Memory (from *Cats*) 70

Nothing Compares 2 U Sinead O'Connor 72

Patience Take That 76

Red Red Wine UB40 78

Run Leona Lewis 80

She's The One Robbie Williams 82

Some Might Say Oasis 86

Somethin' Stupid Frank & Nancy Sinatra 89

Sunny Afternoon The Kinks 92

This Year's Love David Gray 98

Thriller Michael Jackson 100

A Thousand Miles Vanessa Carlton 67

Tide Is High (Get The Feeling) Atomic Kitten 102

Toxic Britney Spears 106

Try A Little Tenderness Otis Redding 112

Unchained Melody The Righteous Brothers 114

Waterloo Abba 118

What A Wonderful World Louis Armstrong 95

When You Say Nothing At All Ronan Keating 122

A Whole New World (from *Aladdin*) 124

You'll Never Walk Alone (from *Carousel*) 126

American Pie

Words & Music by Don McLean

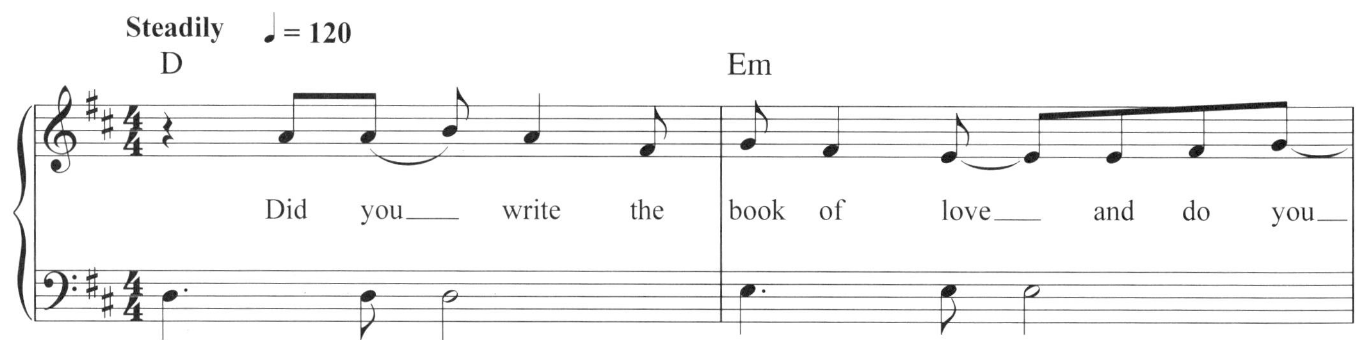

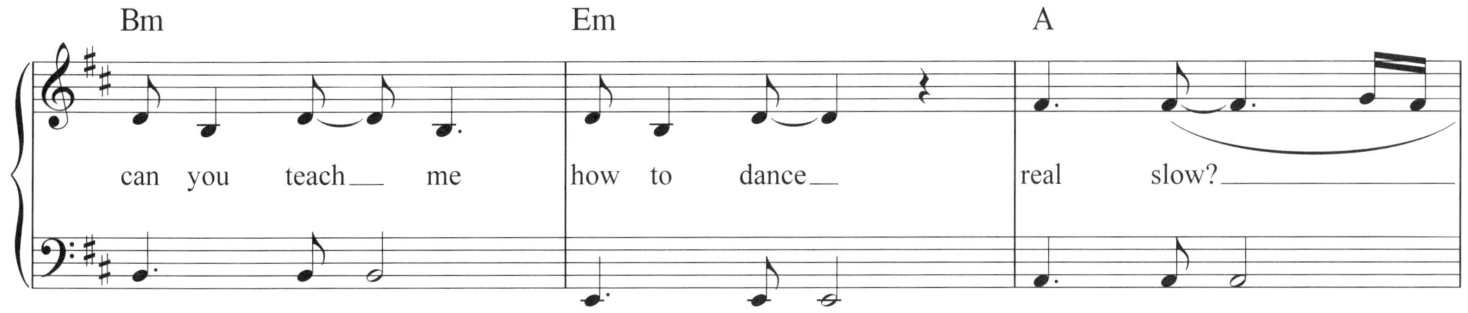
Bm
Em
A
can you teach — me
how to dance —
real slow? —

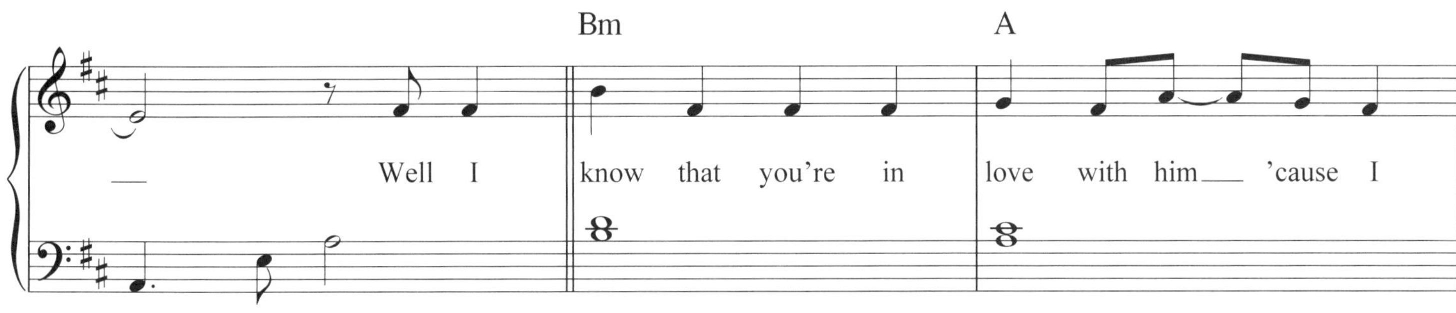
Bm
A
— Well I
know that you're in
love with him — 'cause I

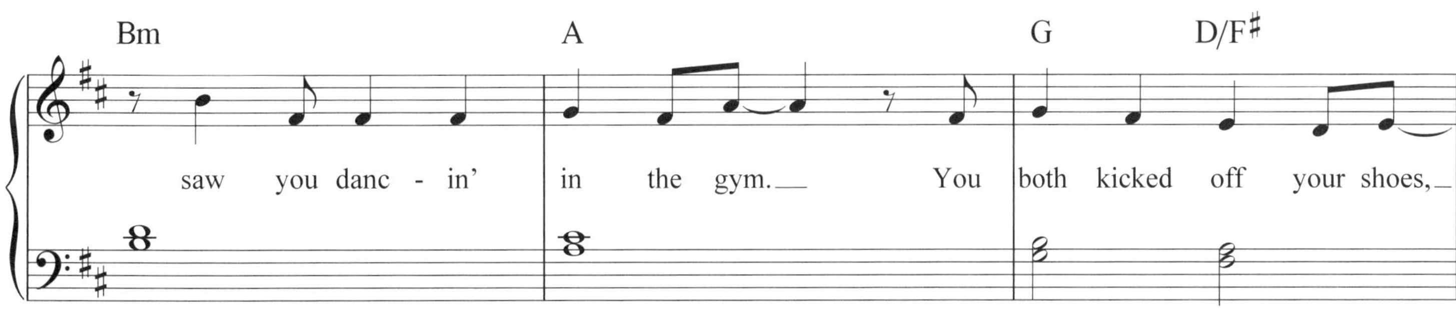
Bm
A
G
D/F♯
saw you danc - in'
in the gym. — You
both kicked off your shoes, —

Em
G
A
— man, I
dig those rhy - thm and blues! —
I was a

D
F♯m/C♯
Bm
Em
lone - ly teen - age
bronc - in' buck, with a
pink car - na - tion and a

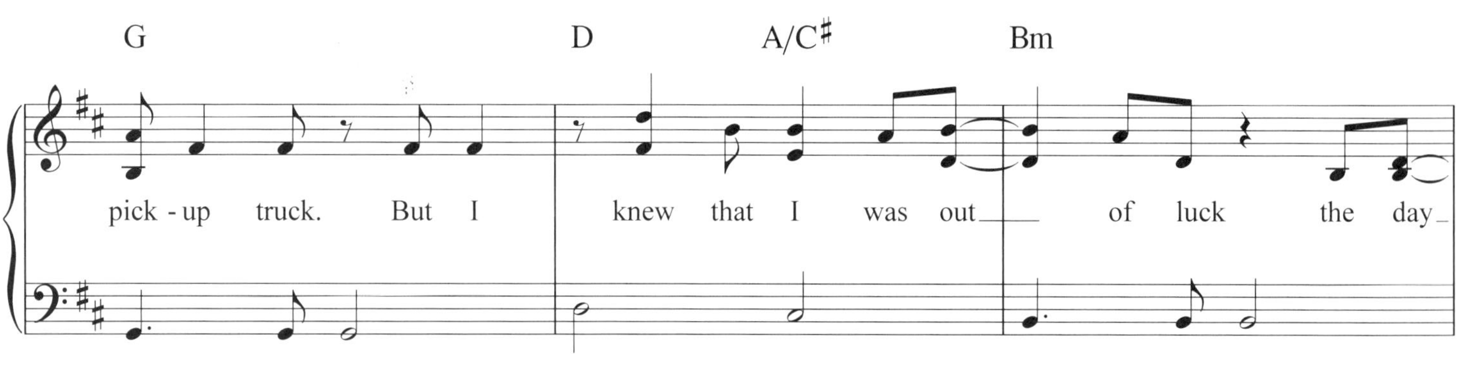
G
D
A/C♯
Bm
pick - up truck. But I
knew that I was out
of luck the day

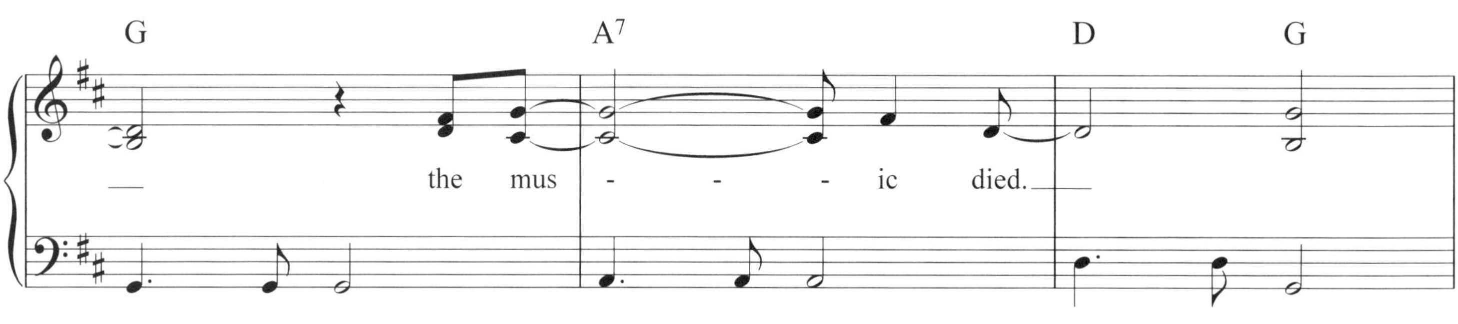
G
A7
D
G
the mus - - - ic died.

D
A
D
G
D
A
I start - ed sing - ing:
Bye - bye Miss A - mer - i - can Pie, drove my

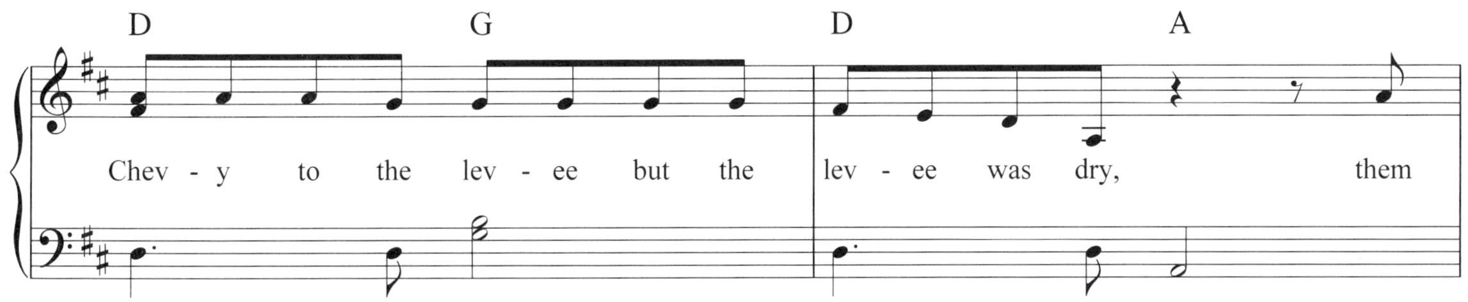

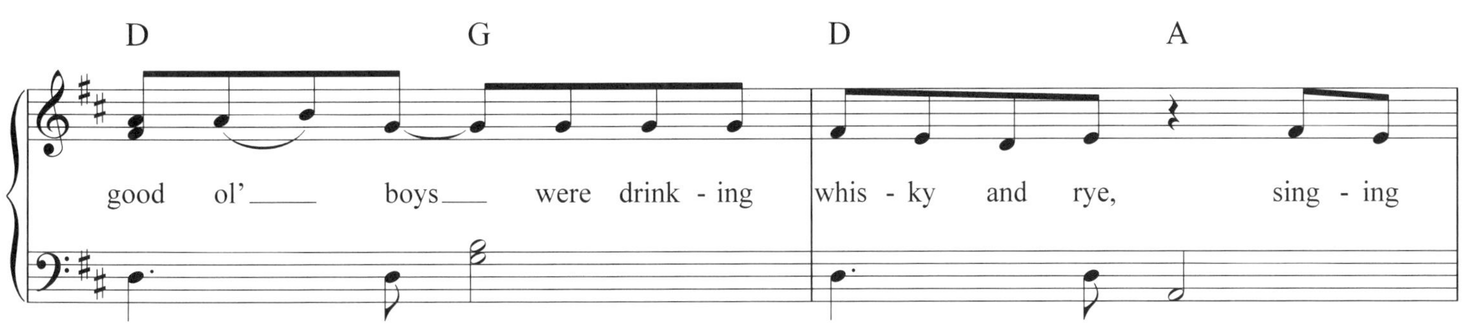

Repeat and fade

All You Need Is Love

Words & Music by John Lennon & Paul McCartney

D
G
D
D7/E
3
3
3
Noth-ing you can say but you can learn how to play the game. It's

D7
1, 2.
3.
eas - y.
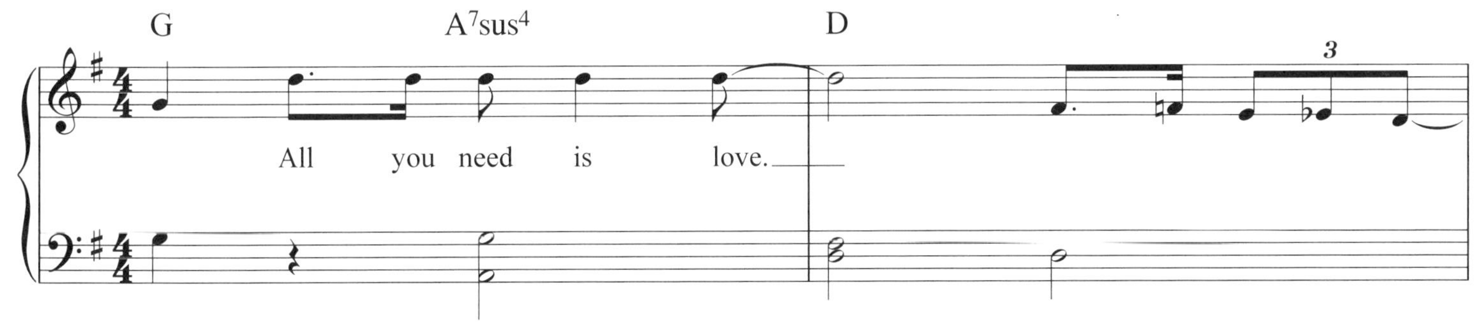
G
A7sus4
D
3
All you need is love.
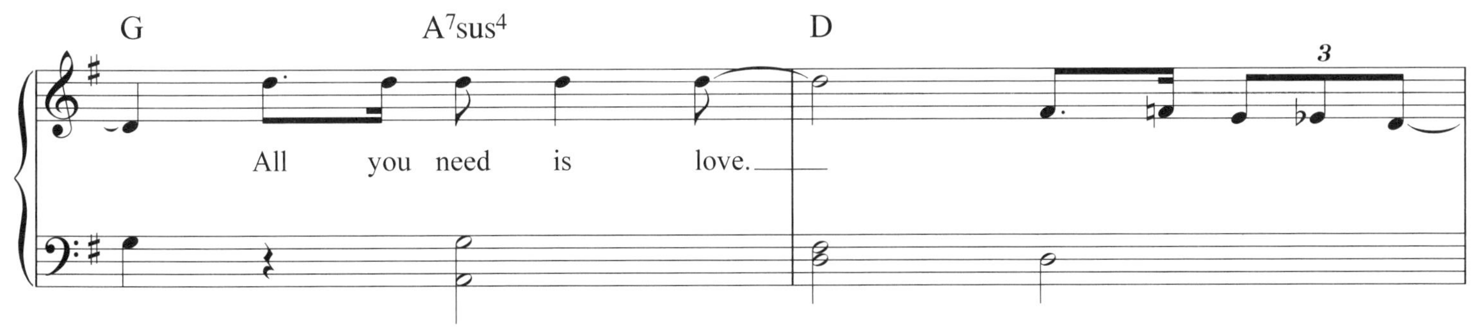
G
A7sus4
D
3
All you need is love.
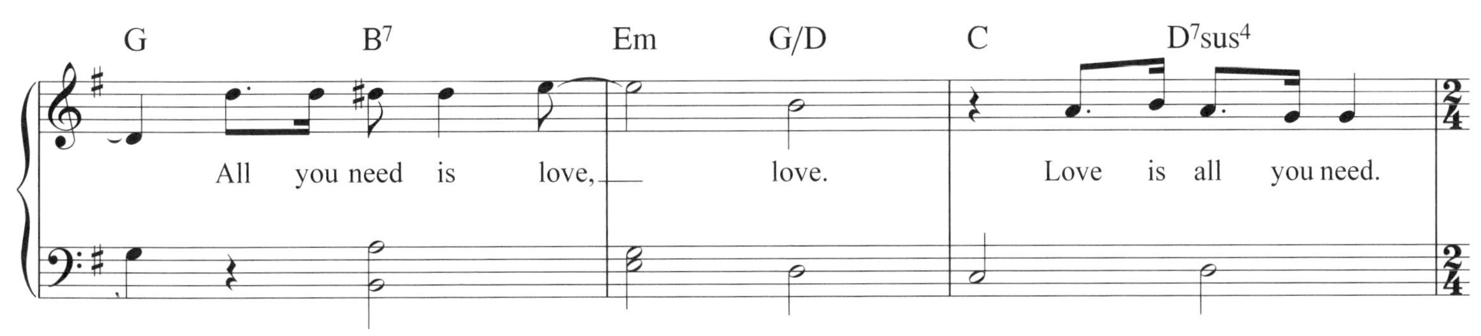
G
B7
Em
G/D
C
D7sus4
All you need is love, love. Love is all you need.

Verse 2:
There's nothing you can make that can't be made.
No one you can save that can't be saved.
Nothing you can do but you can learn how to be you in time.
It's easy.

Verse 3:
There's nothing you can know that isn't known.
Nothing you can see that isn't shown.
Nowhere you can be that isn't where you're meant to be.
It's easy.

Beautiful

Words & Music by Linda Perry

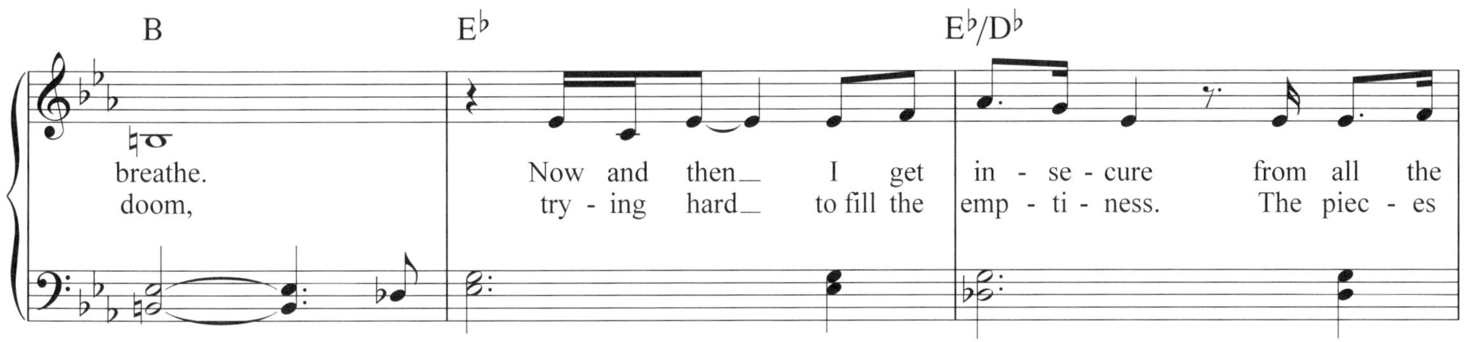

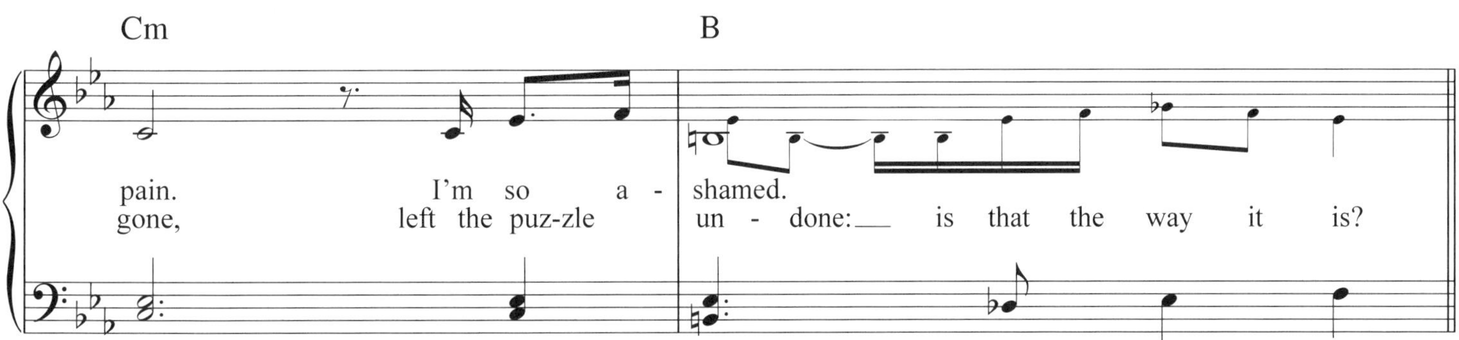

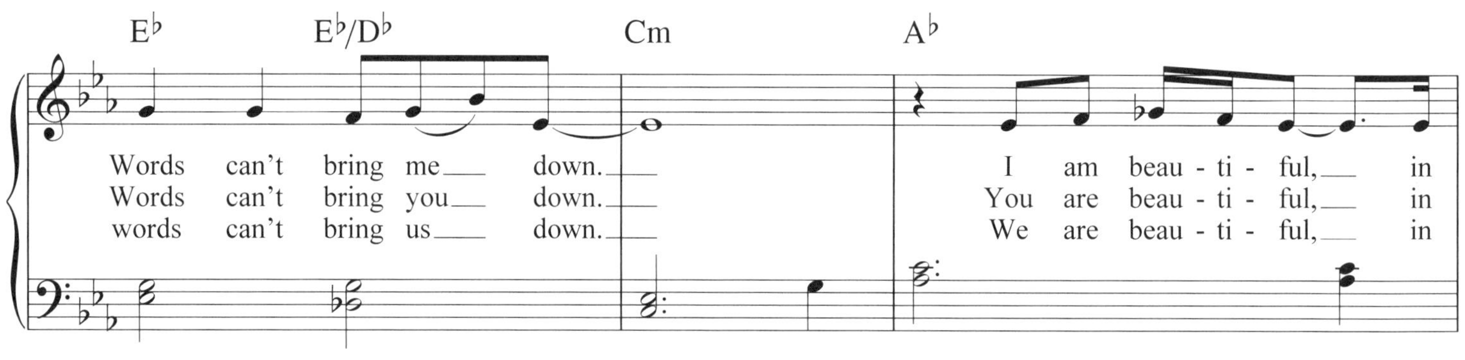
E♭ E♭/D♭ Cm A♭
Words can't bring me down. I am beau - ti - ful, in
Words can't bring you down. You are beau - ti - ful, in
words can't bring us down. We are beau - ti - ful, in

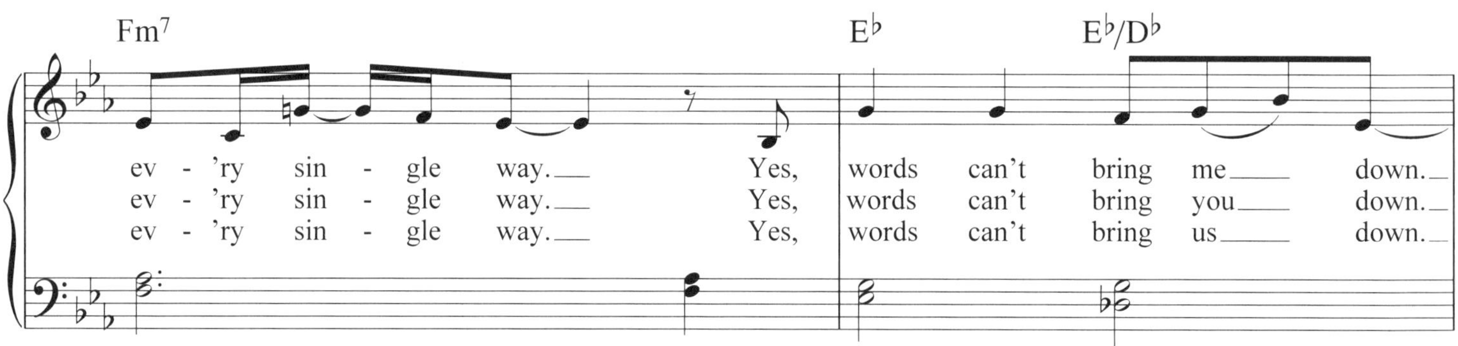
Fm7 E♭ E♭/D♭
ev - 'ry sin - gle way. Yes, words can't bring me down.
ev - 'ry sin - gle way. Yes, words can't bring you down.
ev - 'ry sin - gle way. Yes, words can't bring us down.

1-3.
To Coda
Cm Fm7 E♭
Oh, no.
Oh, no.
Oh, no.
So don't you bring me down to - day.

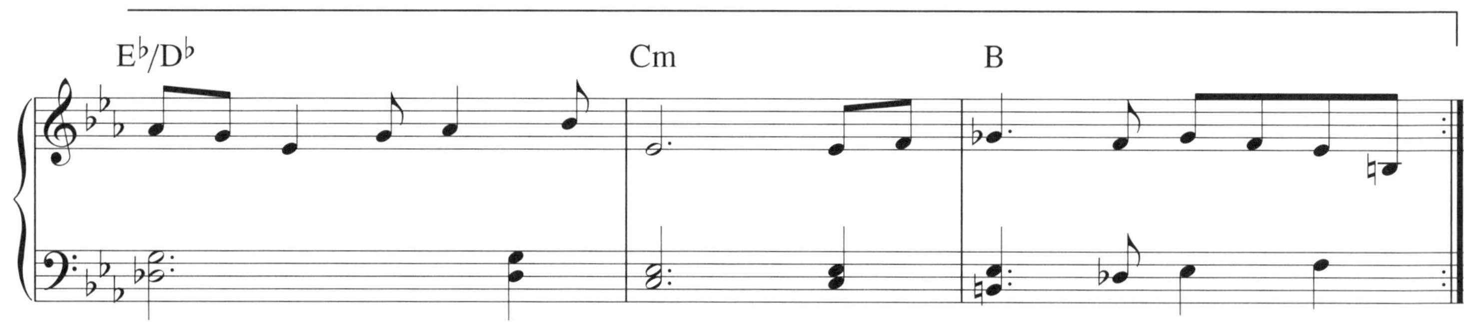
E♭/D♭ Cm B

4.
E♭ E♭/D♭
- day. No mat - ter what we do, no mat - ter what we say,

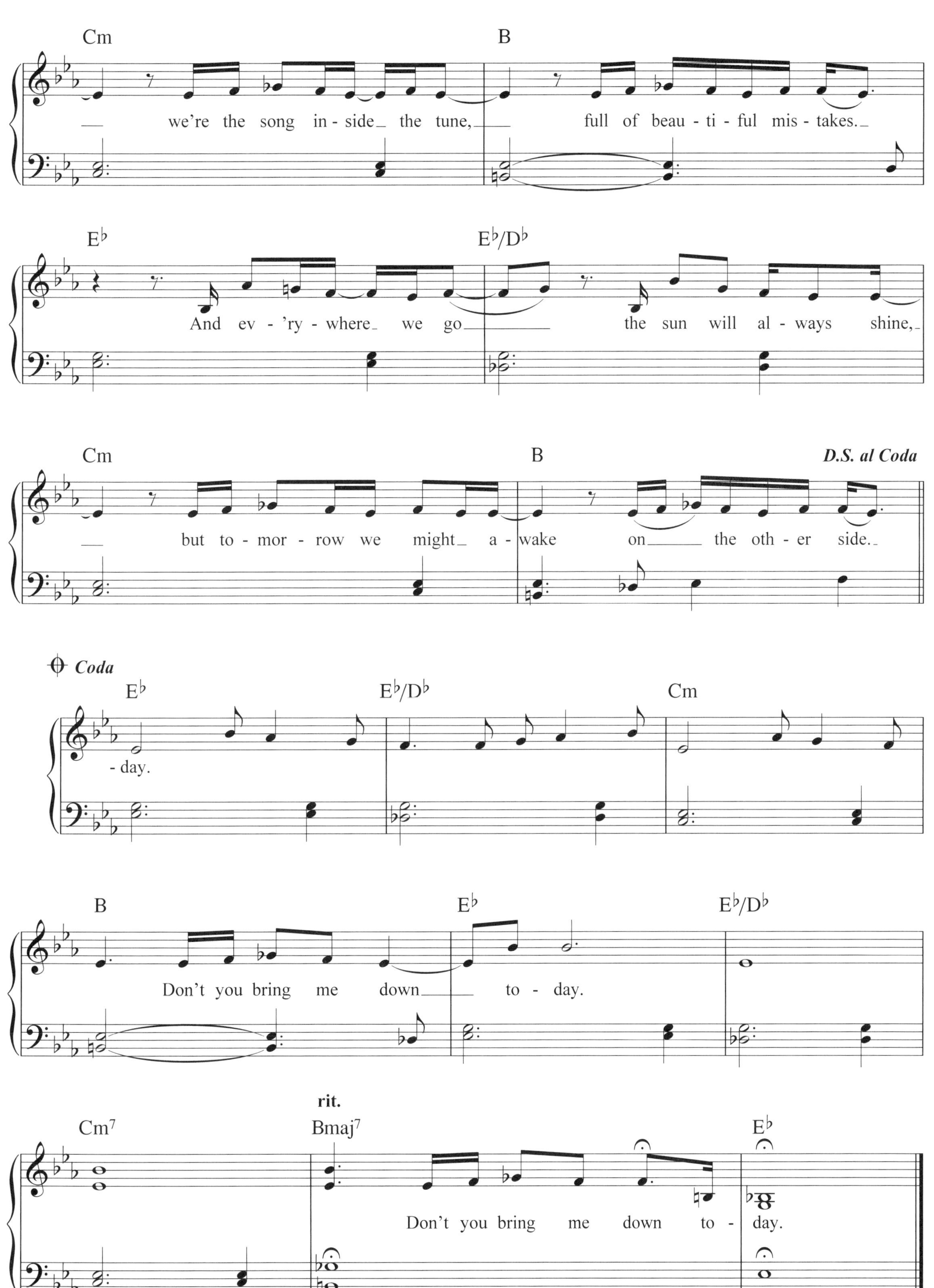
Cm
B
we're the song in - side the tune,
full of beau - ti - ful mis - takes.
E♭
E♭/D♭
And ev - 'ry - where we go
the sun will al - ways shine,
Cm
B
D.S. al Coda
but to - mor - row we might a - wake
on the oth - er side.
Coda
E♭
E♭/D♭
Cm
- day.
B
E♭
E♭/D♭
Don't you bring me down to - day.
rit.
Cm7
Bmaj7
E♭
Don't you bring me down to - day.

The Bare Necessities

Music by Terry Gilkyson

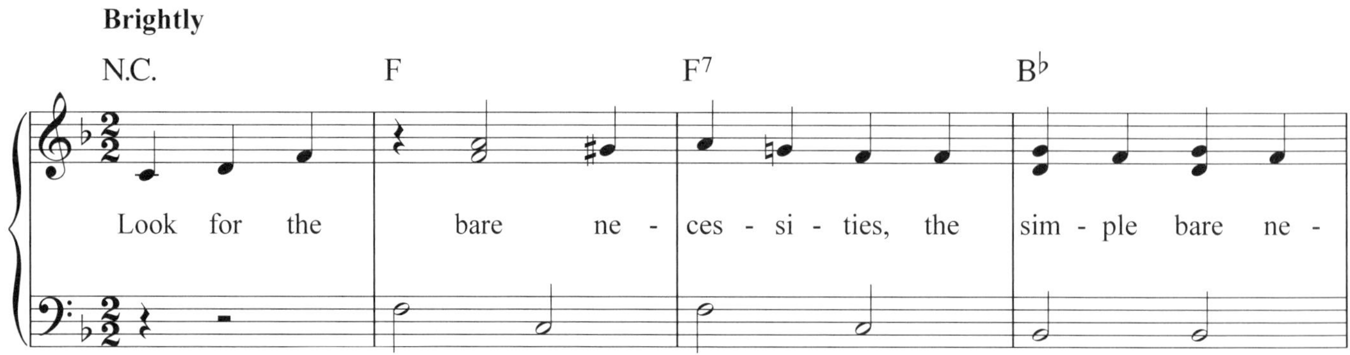

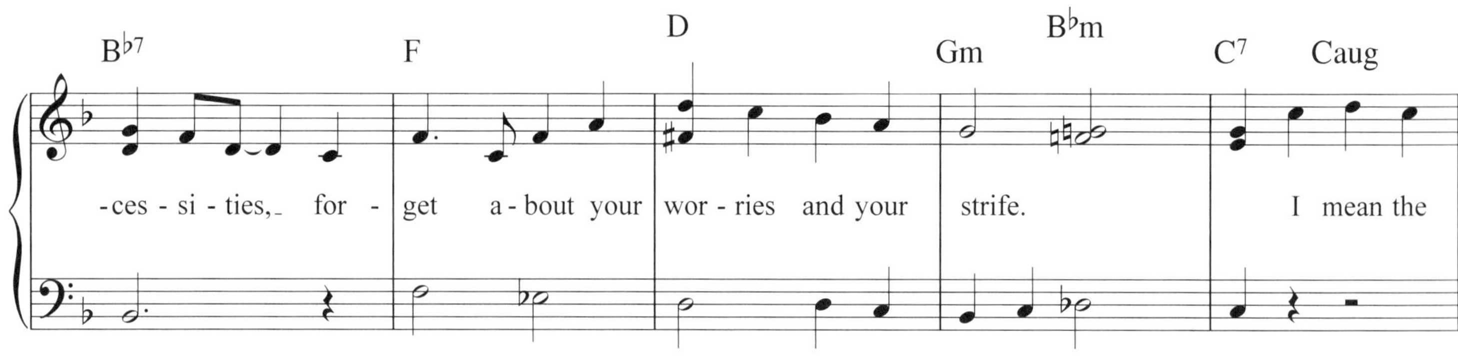

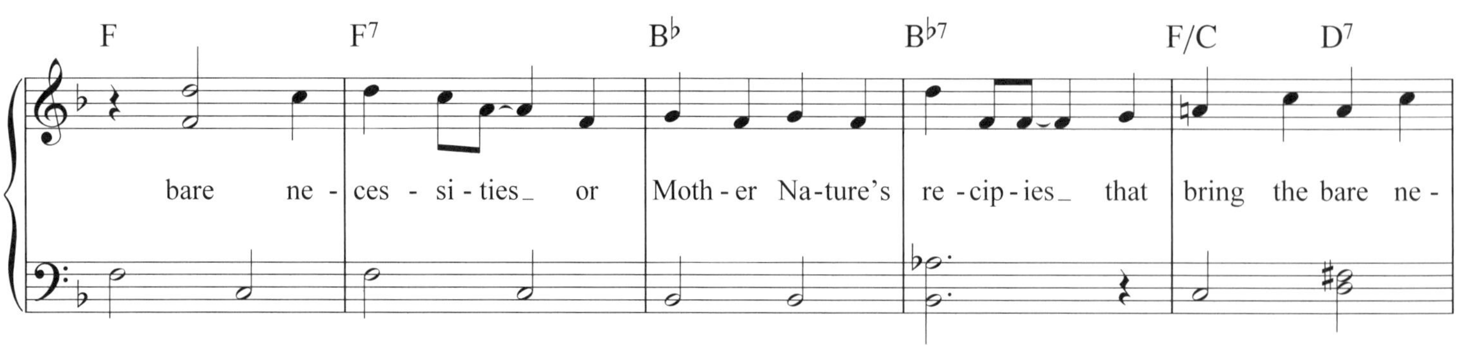

G7 C7 F C7
-ces - si - ties of life. Wher-ev - er I wan - der,

F C7
wher-ev-er I roam, I could-n't be fon - der of my big

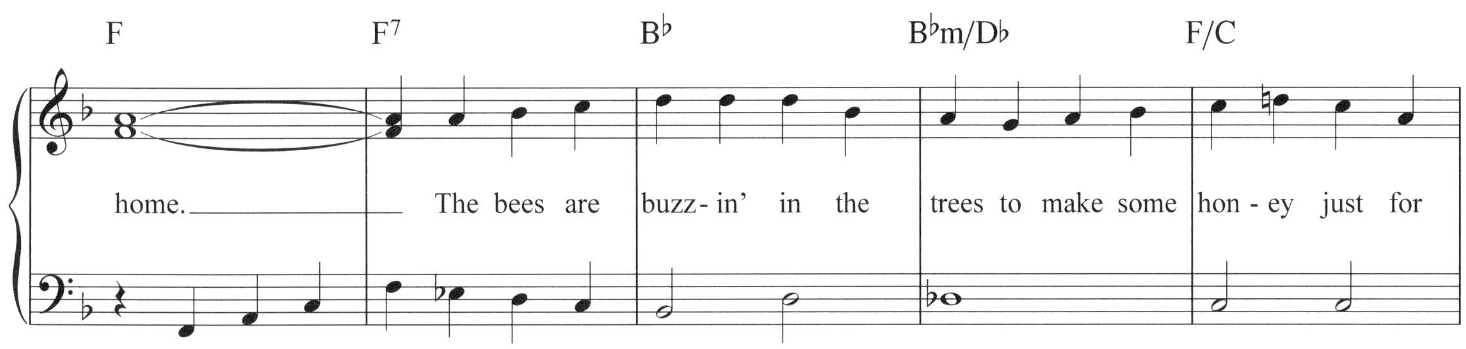
F F7 B♭ B♭m/D♭ F/C
home. The bees are buzz-in' in the trees to make some hon - ey just for

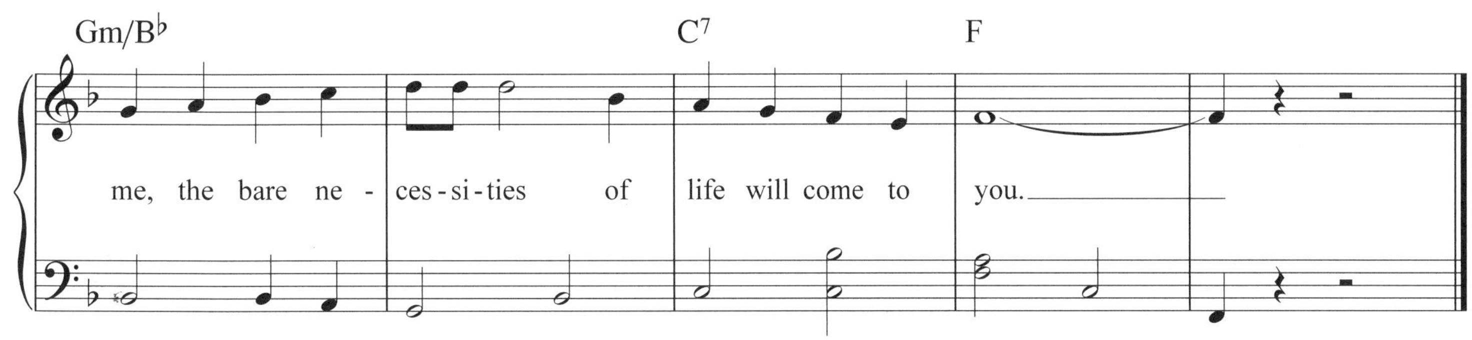
Gm/B♭ C7 F
me, the bare ne - ces-si-ties of life will come to you.

Big Sur

Words by Conor Deasy
Music by Conor Deasy, Kevin Horan, Pádraic McMahon,
Daniel Ryan & Ben Carrigan
Contains elements from "Theme From The Monkees" –
Words & Music by Tommy Boyce & Bobby Hart

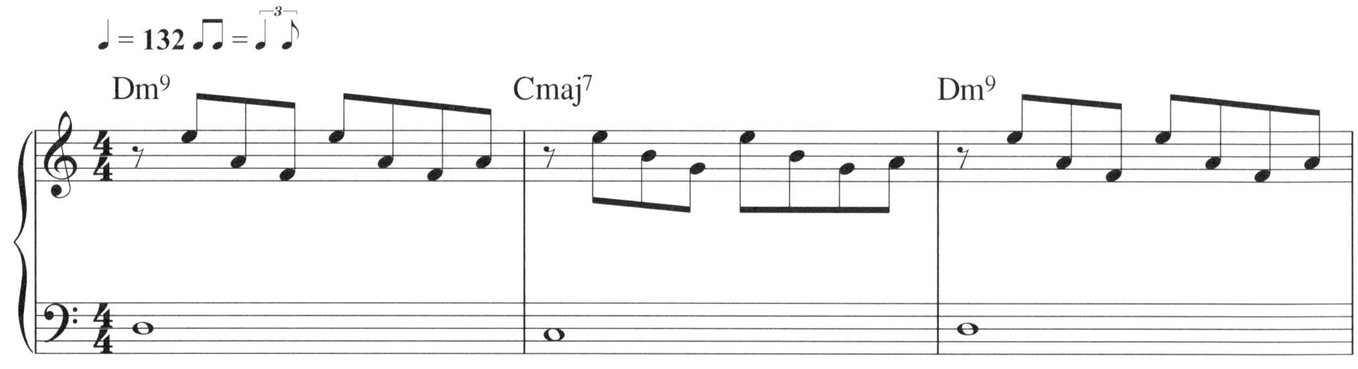

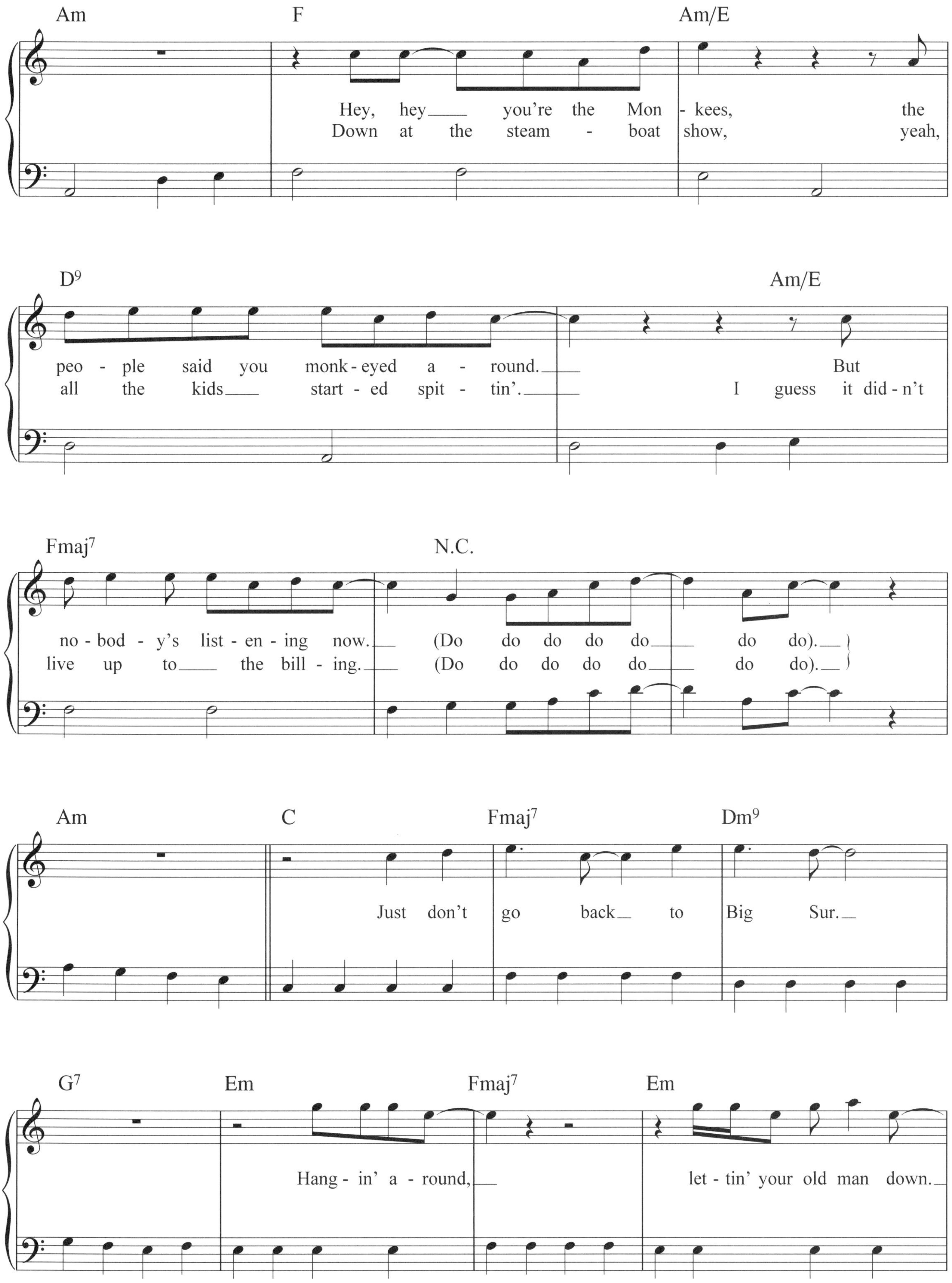

Am F Am/E

Hey, hey you're the Mon - kees, the

Down at the steam - boat show, yeah,

D9 Am/E

peo - ple said you monk - eyed a - round. But

all the kids start - ed spit - tin'. I guess it did - n't

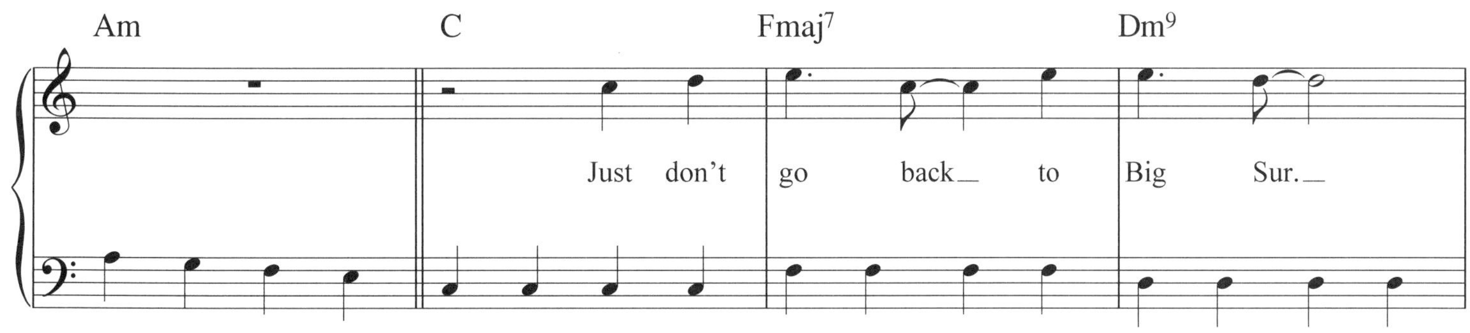

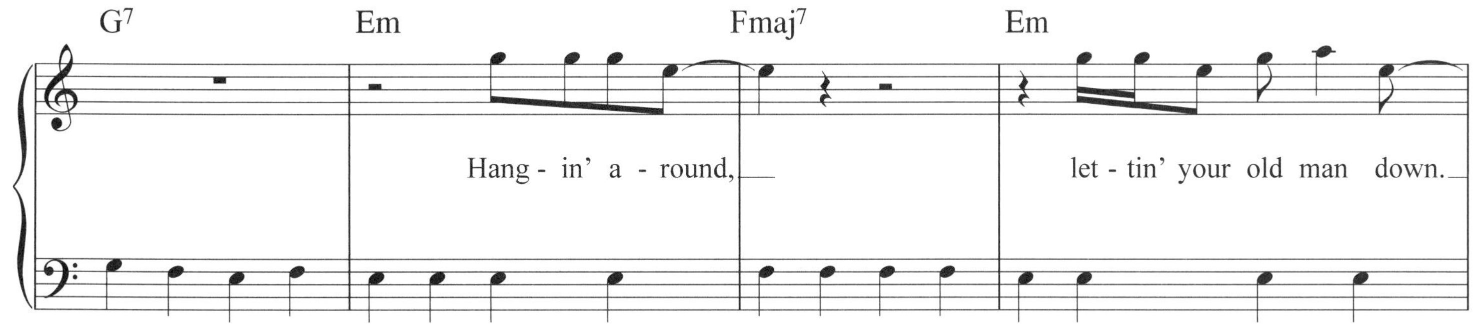

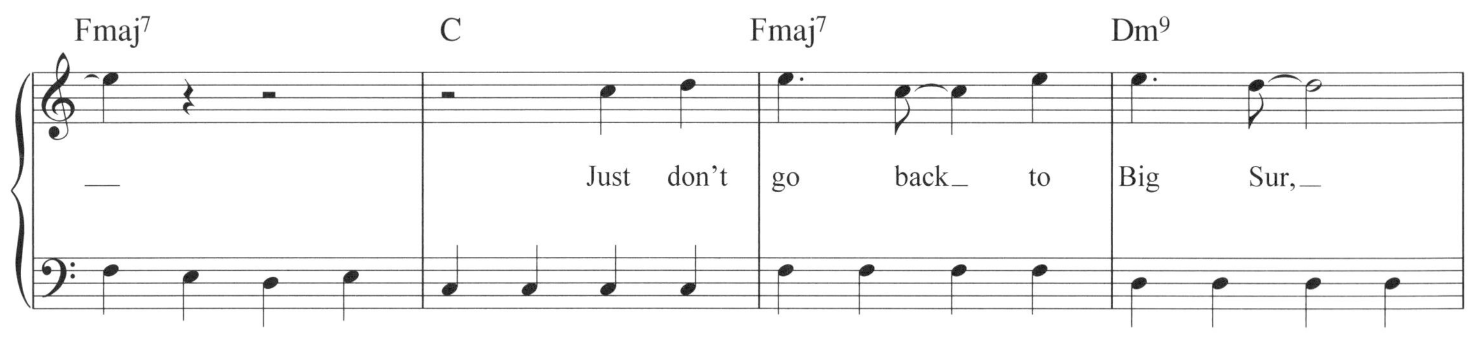
Fmaj7
C
Fmaj7
Dm9
Just don't go back to Big Sur,
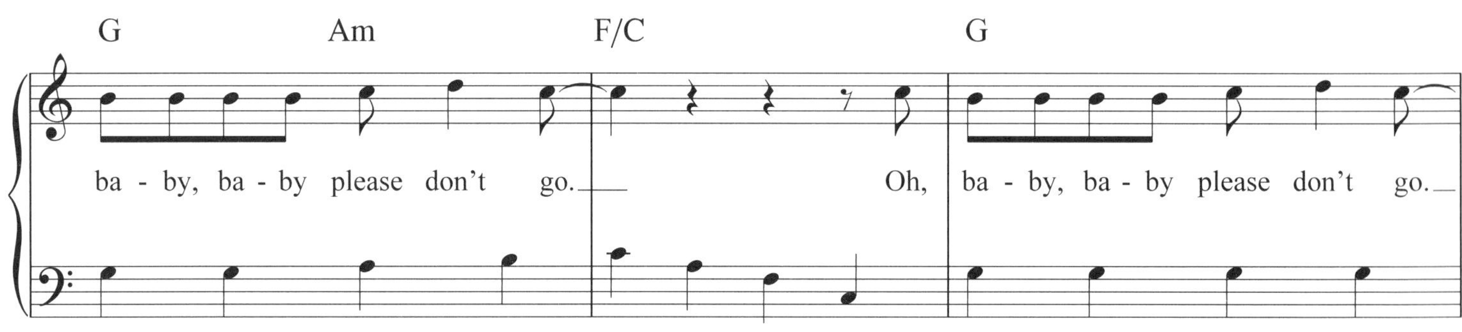
G
Am
F/C
G
ba - by, ba - by please don't go.
Oh,
ba - by, ba - by please don't go.
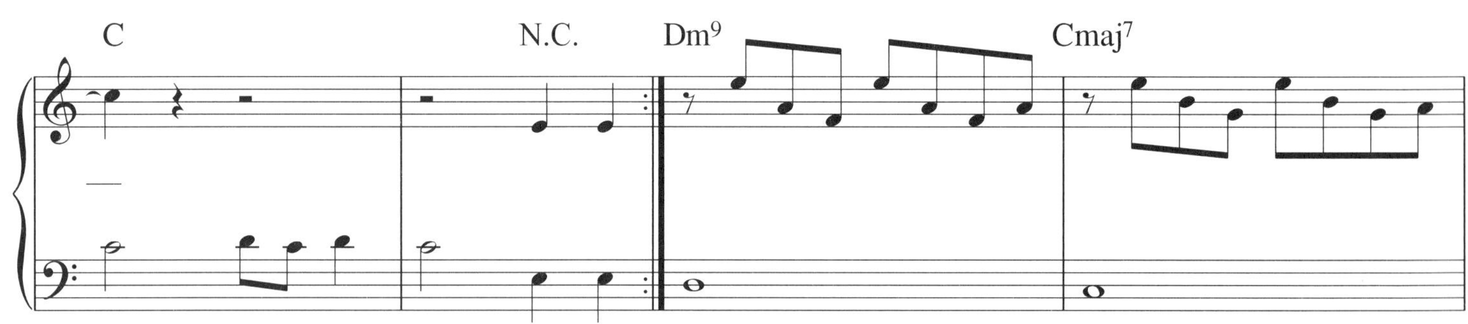
C
N.C.
Dm9
Cmaj7
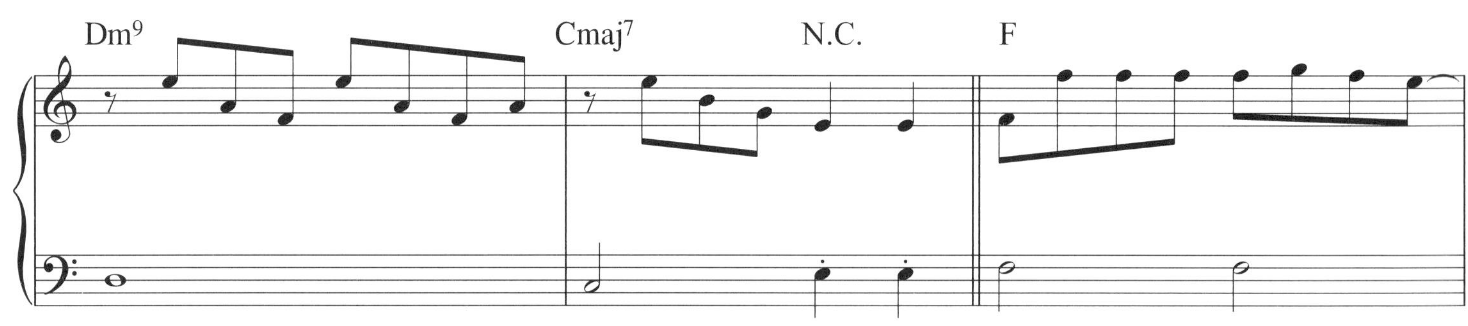
Dm9
Cmaj7
N.C.
F

Am/E
D9
Am/E

F
N.C.
Am
(Do do do do do do do).

C
Fmaj7
Dm9
G
Em
Just don't go back to Big Sur.
Hang - in' a - round,

Fmaj7
Em
Fmaj7
let - tin' your old man down.

C
Fmaj7
Dm9
G
Just don't go back to Big Sur,
ba - by, ba - by please don't go,

F/C
G
C
oh, ba - by, ba - by please don't go.

Big Spender

Words by Dorothy Fields
Music by Cy Coleman

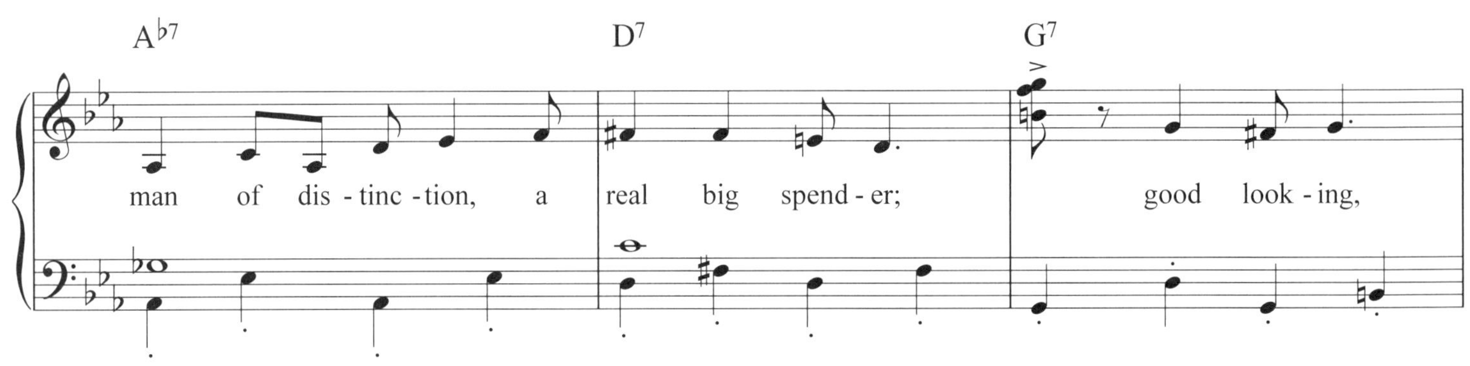

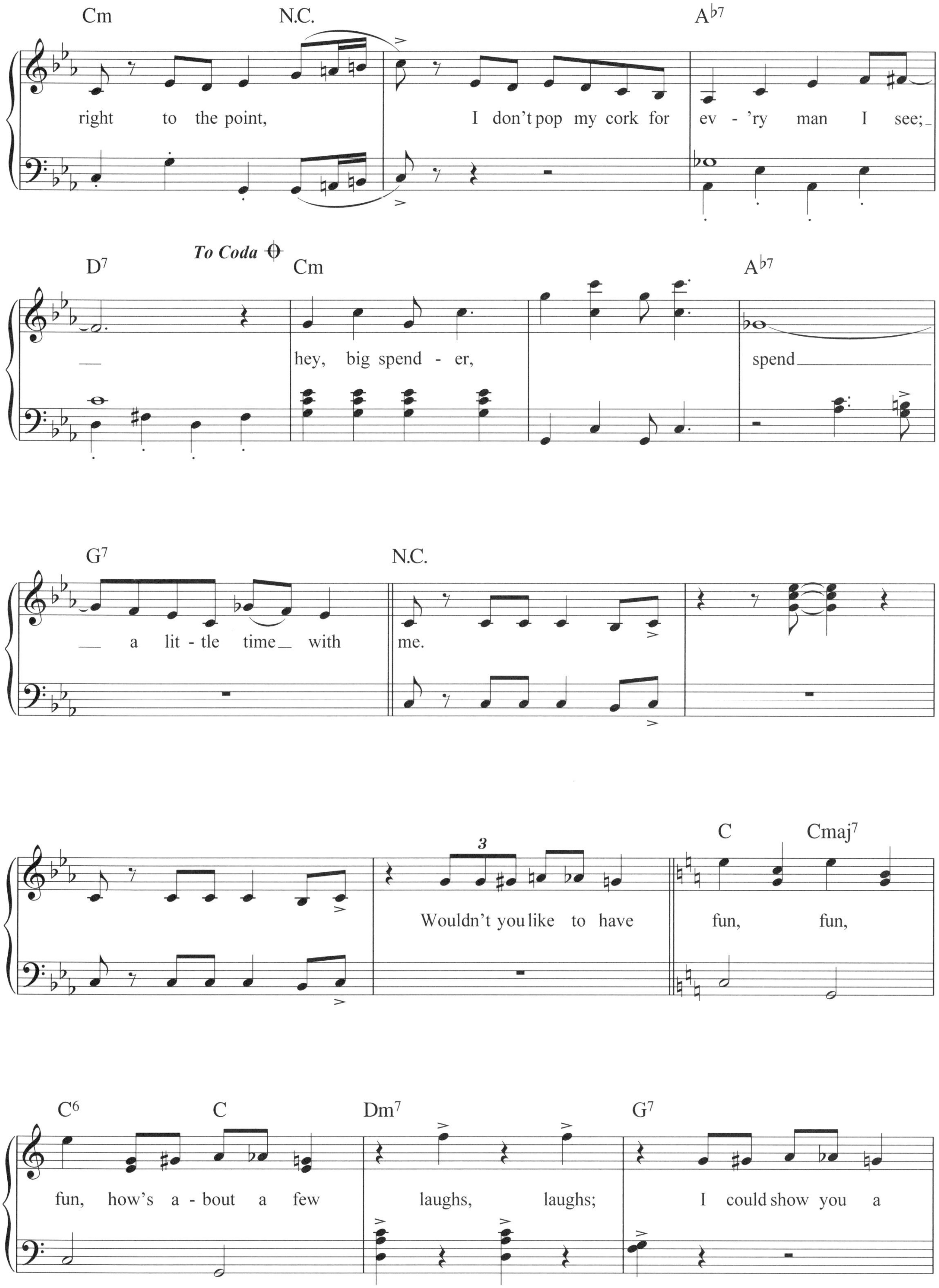

Cm N.C. A♭7

right to the point, I don't pop my cork for ev - 'ry man I see; _

D7 *To Coda* 𝄌 Cm A♭7

__ hey, big spend - er, spend ______________

G7 N.C.

__ a lit - tle time __ with me.

3

Wouldn't you like to have

C Cmaj7

fun, fun,

A♭7
G
A♭7
good time,
let me show you a
good time.

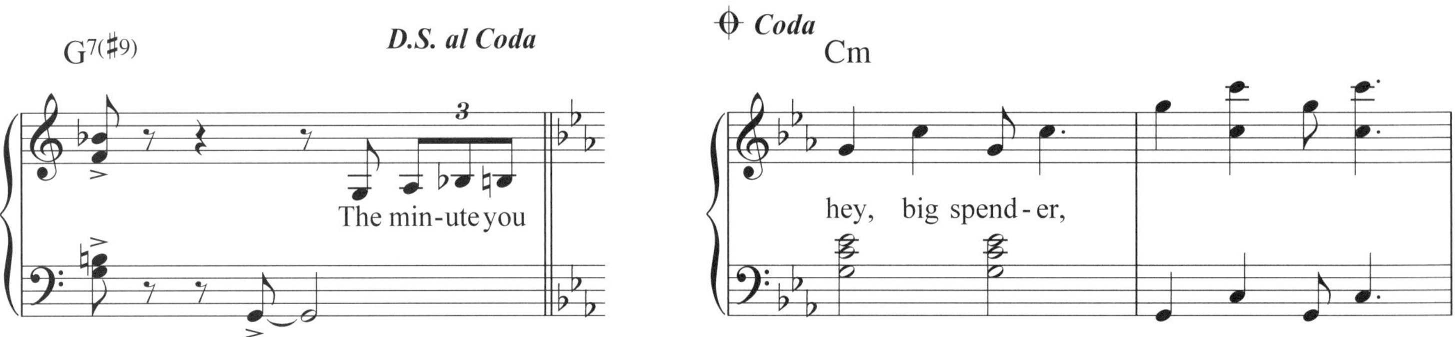
G7(♯9)
D.S. al Coda
Coda
Cm
The min-ute you
hey, big spend-er,

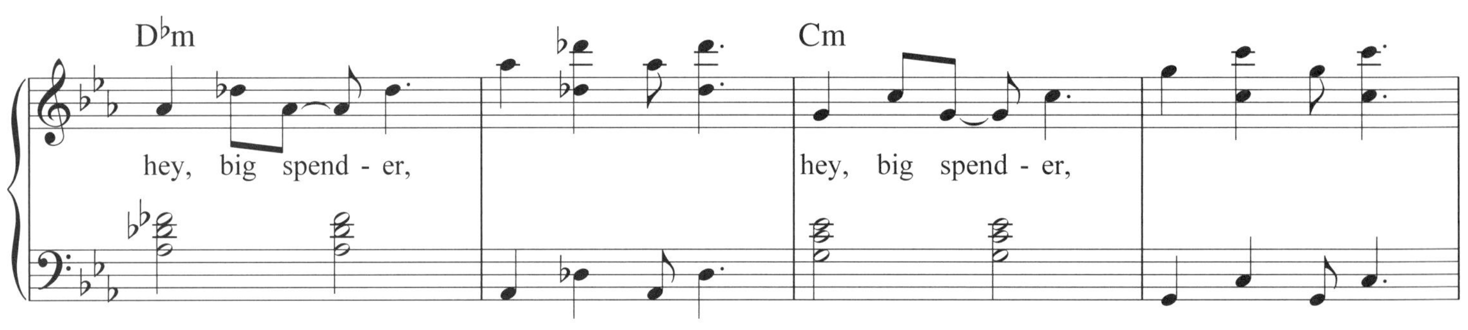
D♭m
Cm
hey, big spend-er,
hey, big spend-er,

A♭7
G7
Cm
Cm/B♭
spend
a lit-tle time with
me.

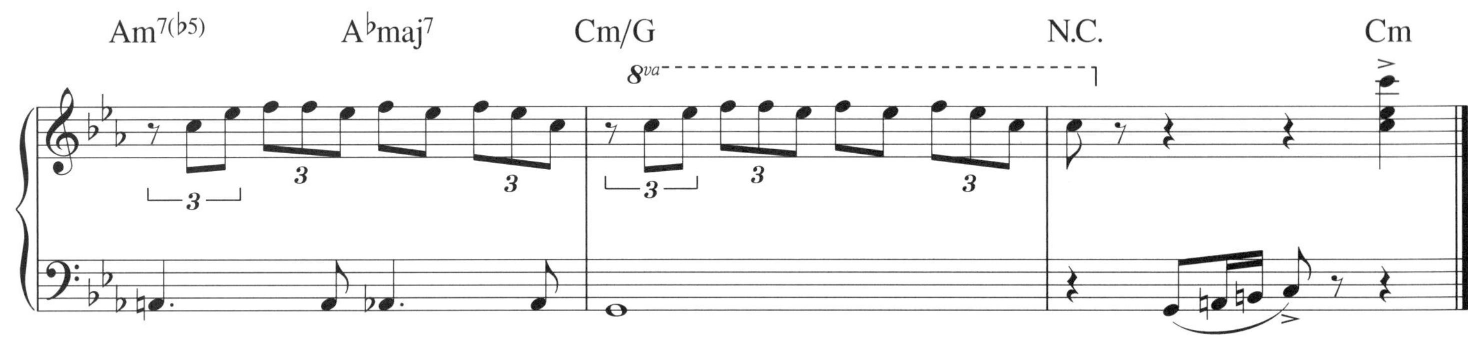
Am7(♭5)
A♭maj7
Cm/G
N.C.
Cm
8va

Breaking Free

Words & Music by Jamie Houston

With energy ♩ = 108

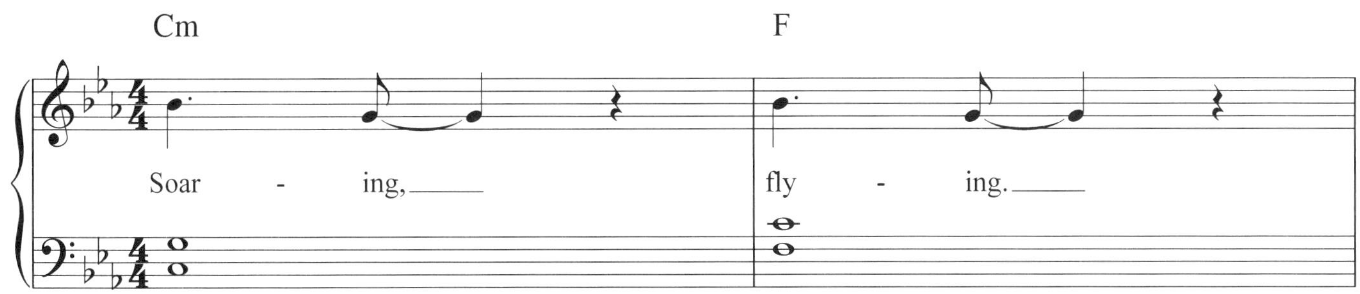

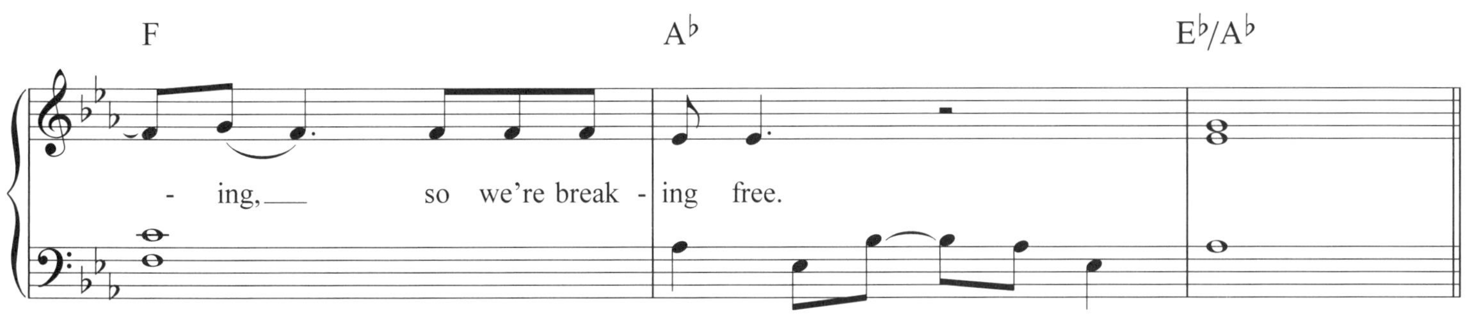

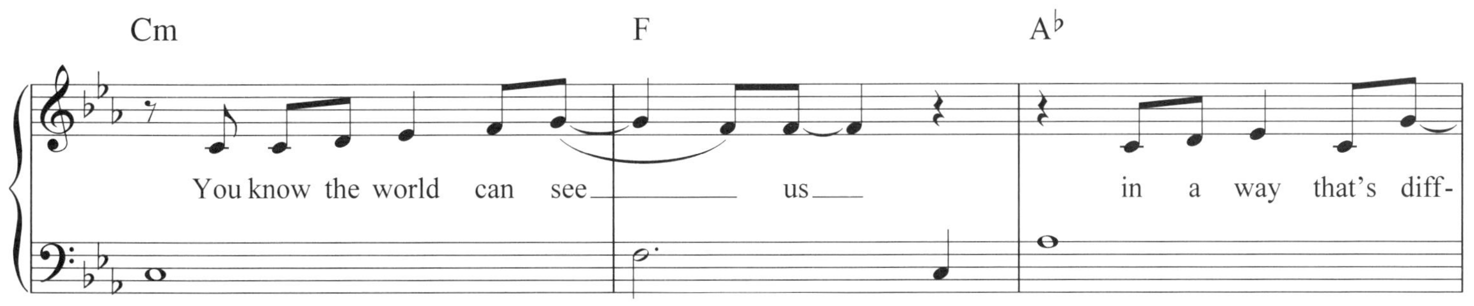

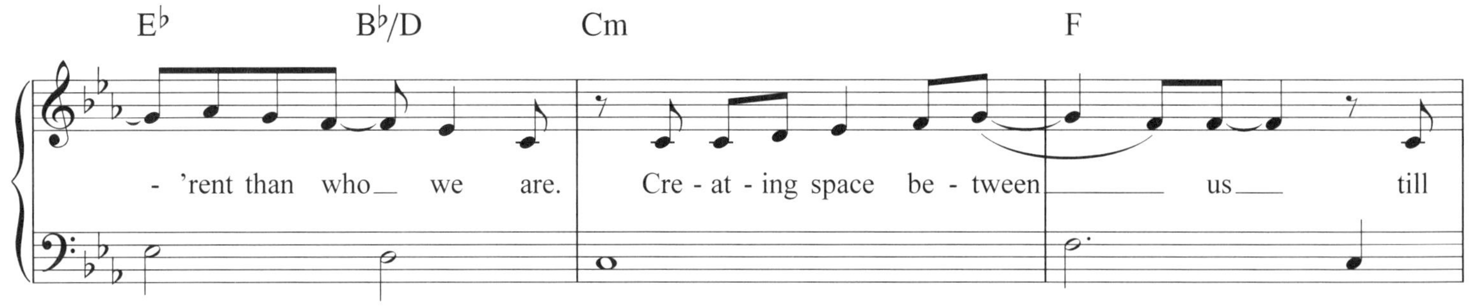

E♭
B♭/D
Cm
F
- 'rent than who we are. Cre - at - ing space be - tween us till

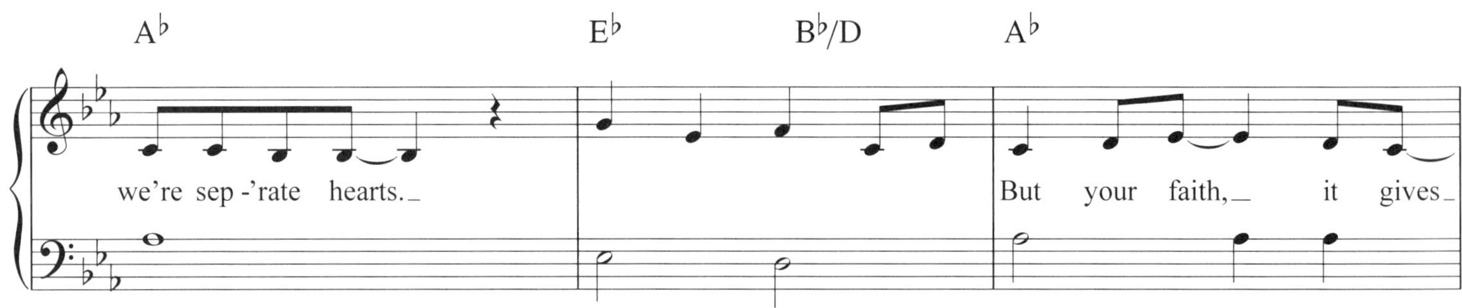

A♭
E♭
B♭/D
A♭
we're sep - 'rate hearts. But your faith, it gives

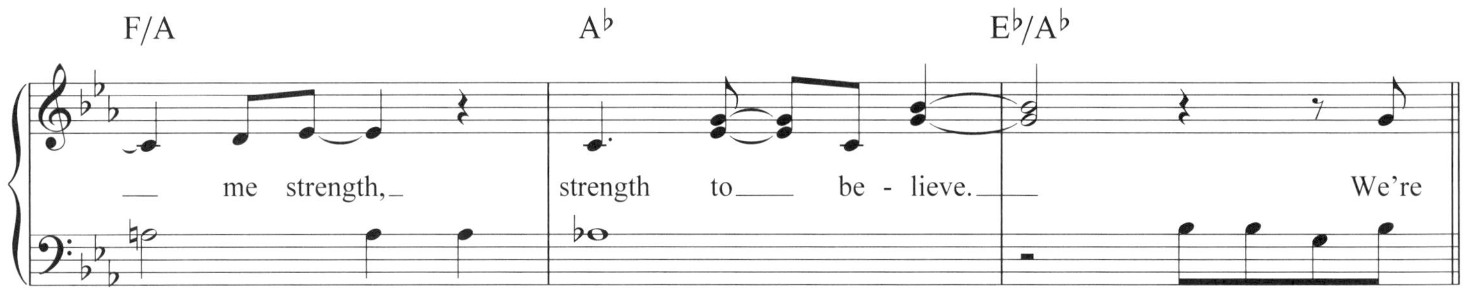

F/A
A♭
E♭/A♭
me strength, strength to be - lieve. We're

Cm
F
A♭
soar - ing, fly - ing. There's not a star in heav -

E♭
B♭/D
Cm
F
- en that we can't reach if we're try - ing, yeah, we're break -

A♭
Cm
- ing free. Oh, we're break - ing free. We're run - ning,

F
A♭
E♭
B♭/D
climb - ing, to get to that place, to be all that we can be.
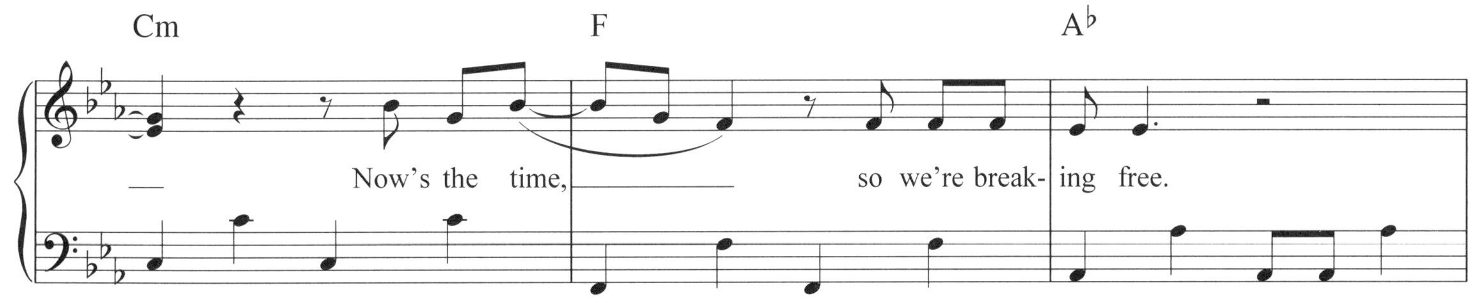
Cm
F
A♭
Now's the time, so we're break- ing free.

Cm
F
Oh.
We know the world can see us
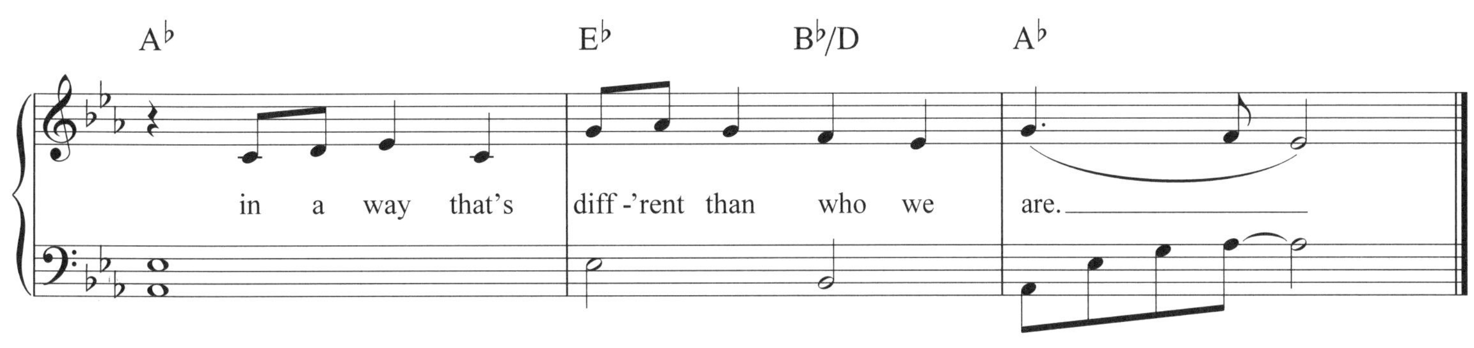
A♭
E♭
B♭/D
A♭
in a way that's diff -'rent than who we are.

Candle In The Wind

Words & Music by Elton John & Bernie Taupin

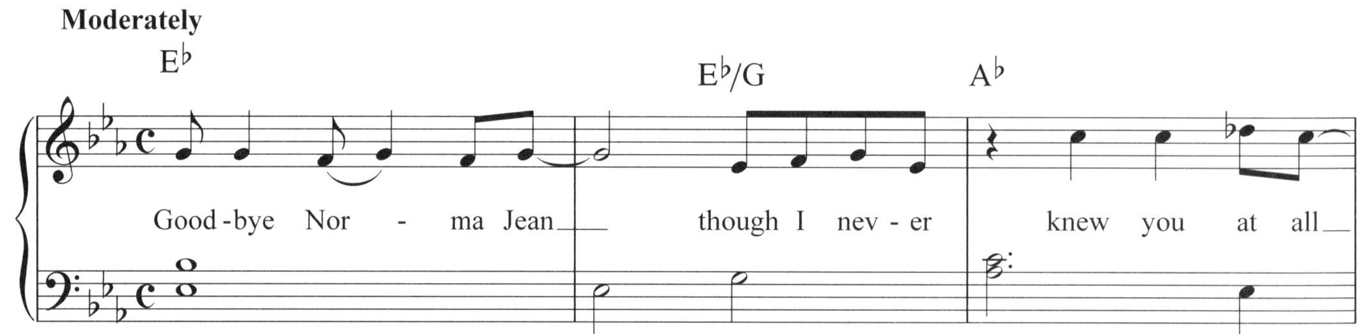

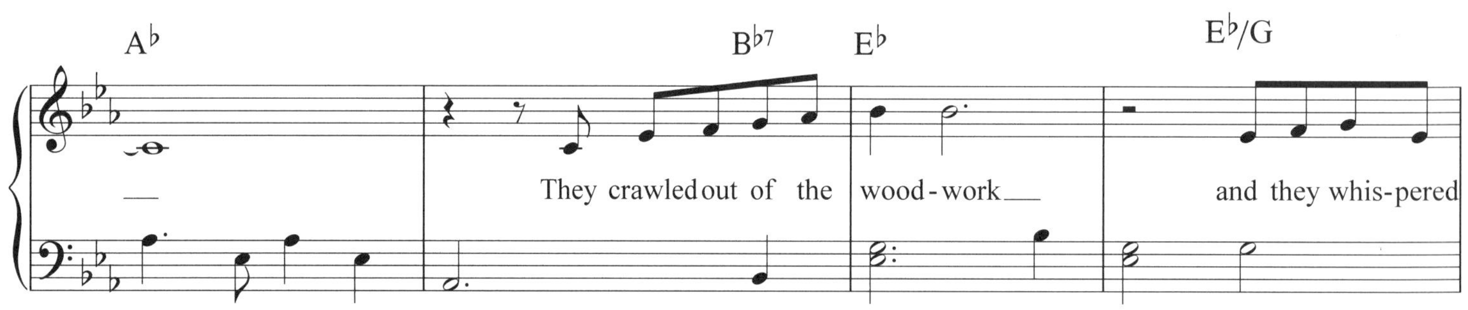

E♭sus4 E♭ Gm7
A♭
B♭/D
made you change your name
And it
seems to me you

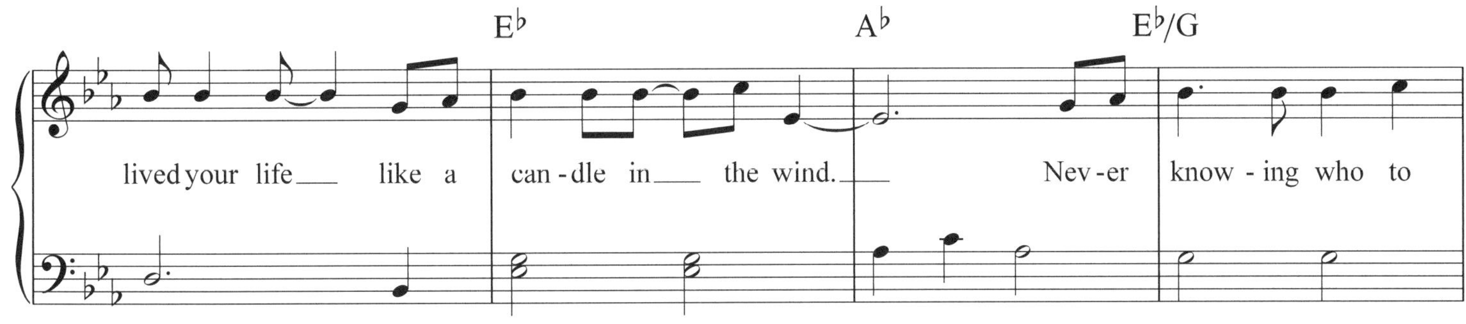
E♭
A♭
E♭/G
lived your life like a
can-dle in the wind.
Nev-er
know-ing who to

E♭ A♭/E♭ E♭ B♭
A♭
cling to when the
rain set in.
And I
would have liked to have known

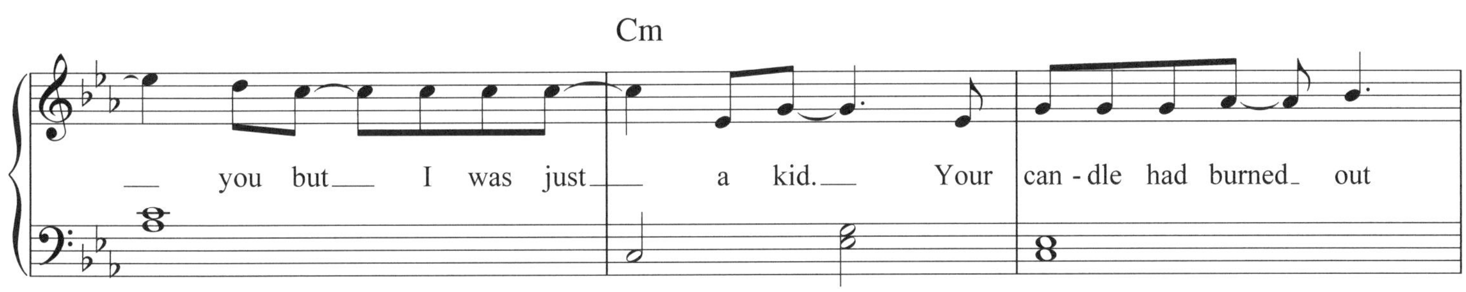
Cm
you but I was just
a kid. Your
can-dle had burned out

B♭
A♭
Gm Fm E♭
long be-fore your
leg-end ev-er did.

Clocks

Words & Music by Guy Berryman, Chris Martin,
Jon Buckland & Will Champion

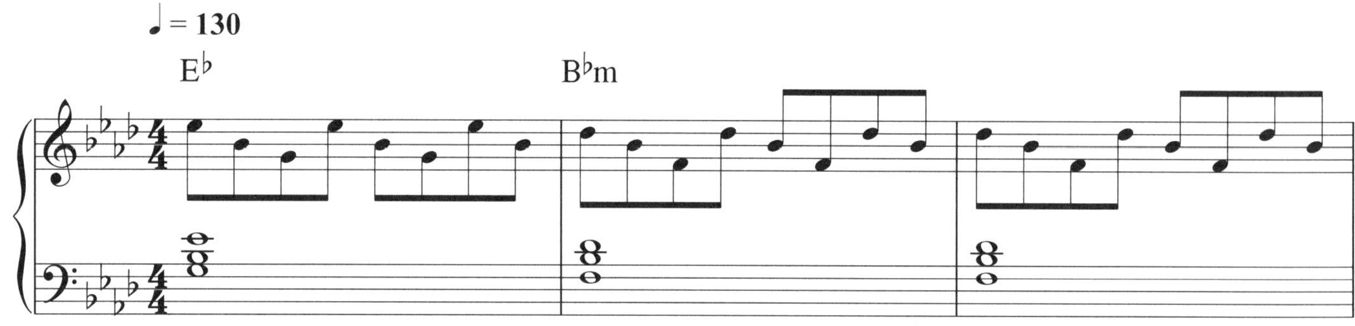

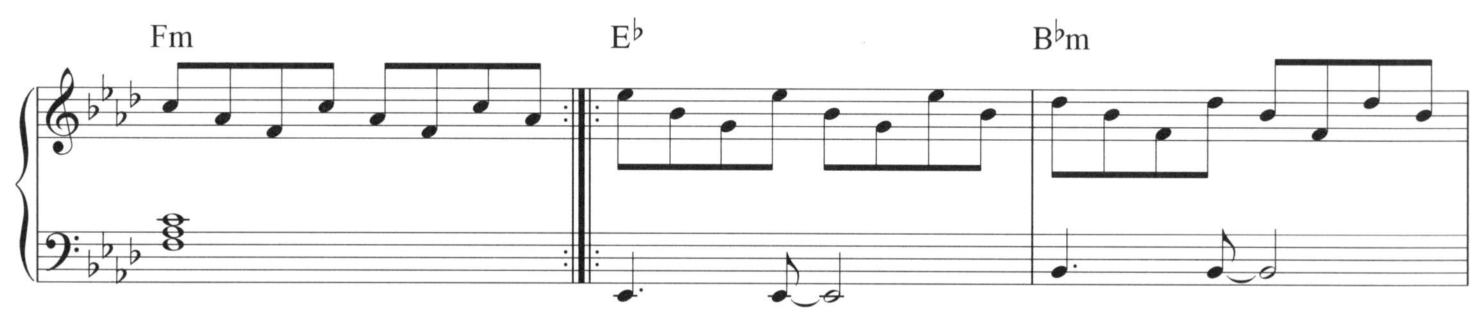

E♭
B♭m
lights go out and I can't be saved, tides that I tried to
2. Con - fu - sion that nev - er stops, the clos - ing walls and
Fm
E♭
B♭m
swim a - gainst have brought me down up - on my knees,
tick - ing clocks: gon - na come back and take you home I
Fm
E♭
oh, I beg, I beg and plead, sing - ing: come out with
could not stop that you now know. Sing - ing: come out up -
B♭m
Fm
things un - said; shoot an ap - ple off my head; and a
- on the seas, curse missed op - por - tu - ni - ties. Am I
E♭
B♭m
trou - ble that can't be named: a ti - ger's wait - ing
a part of the cure, or am I part of

Fm
E♭
B♭m
to be tamed.
the dis - ease?
Sing - ing...
You
Fm
E♭
are.
You
B♭m
Fm
are.
E♭
B♭m
You
are.
Fm
E♭
B♭m
You

Fm
E♭
are.
3° & 4° You
B♭m
Fm
Play 4 times
are.
G♭maj7
And
noth - - - ing else
D♭
A♭6
com - pares,
G♭maj7
and
noth - - - ing else

D♭
A♭6
com - pares,
G♭maj7
and noth - - - - ing else
D♭
A♭6
com - pares.
G♭maj7
E♭
B♭m

Fm
E♭
3° & 4° You
B♭m
Fm
Play 4 times
are.
E♭
B♭m
Home,
home,
where I
Fm
Play 4 times
E♭
want - ed to
go.
B♭m
Fm
Repeat to fade

Crazy

Words & Music by Willie Nelson

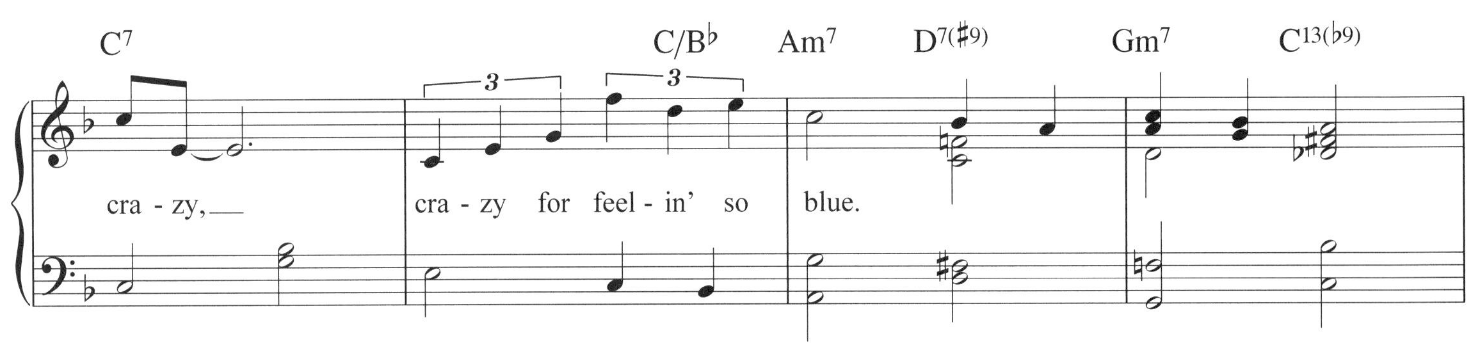

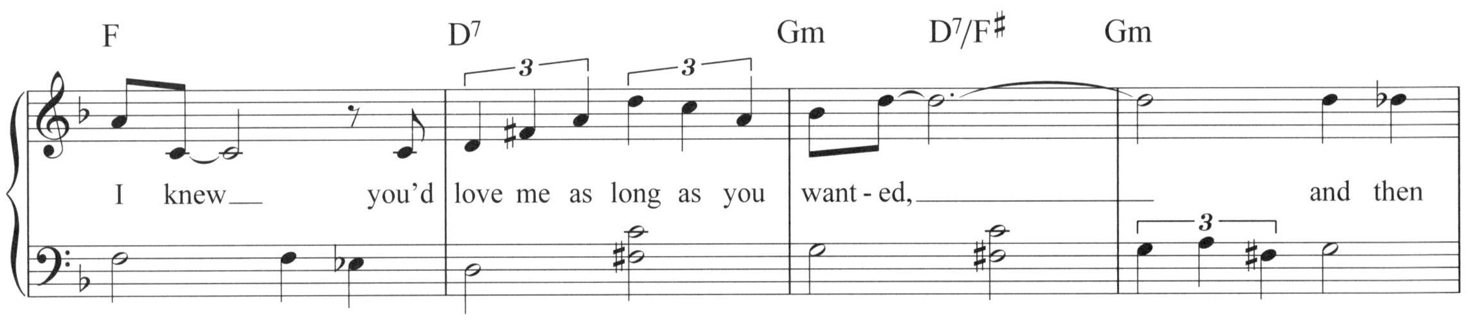

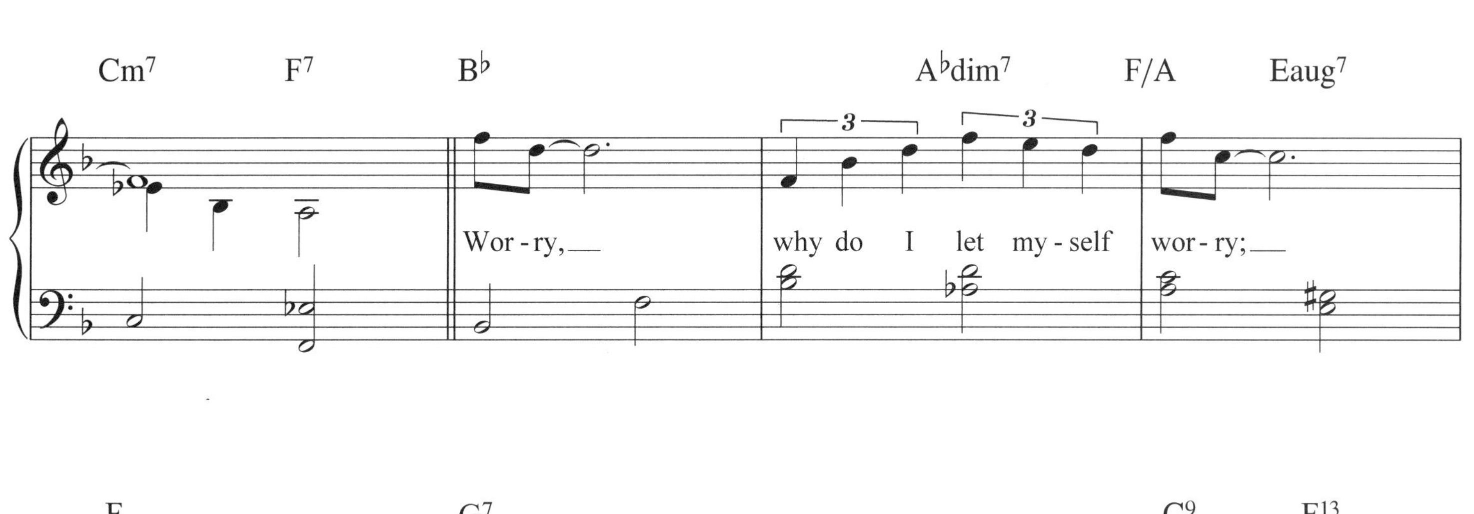
Cm7 F7 B♭ A♭dim7 F/A Eaug7
3 3
Wor - ry,
why do I let my - self
wor - ry;

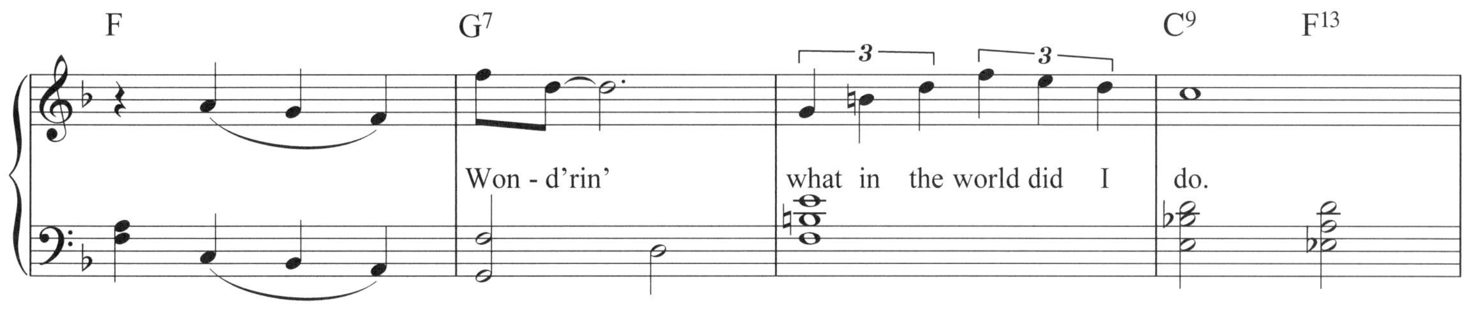
F G7 C9 F13
3 3
Won - d'rin'
what in the world did I
do.

B♭9 E♭13 F D7
3 3
Cra - zy, for
think - ing that my love could

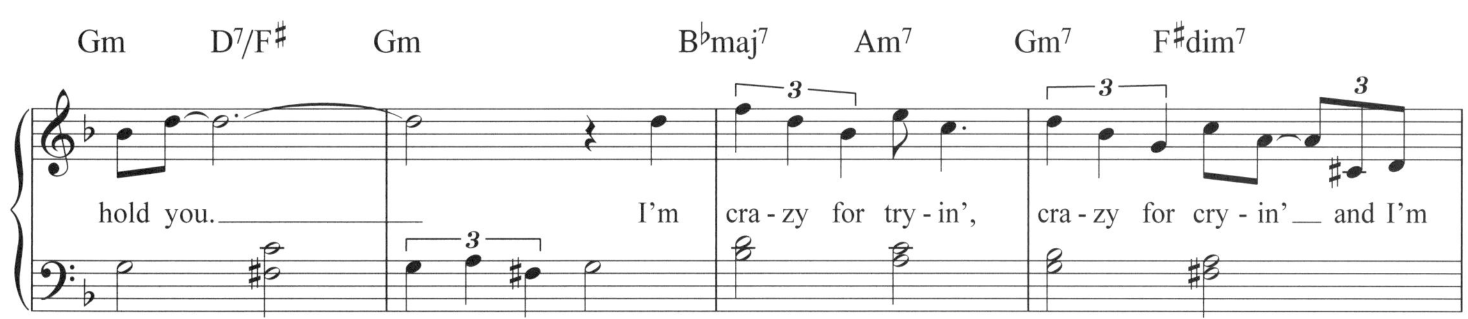
Gm D7/F♯ Gm B♭maj7 Am7 Gm7 F♯dim7
3 3 3 3
hold you. I'm
cra - zy for try - in',
cra - zy for cry - in' and I'm

1. 2.
Gm7 C13 F E♭13 D♭13 Caug7 F G♭6/9 F6/9
3
cra - zy for lov - in'
you.
you.

Can't Help Falling In Love

Words & Music by George David Weiss,
Hugo Peretti & Luigi Creatore

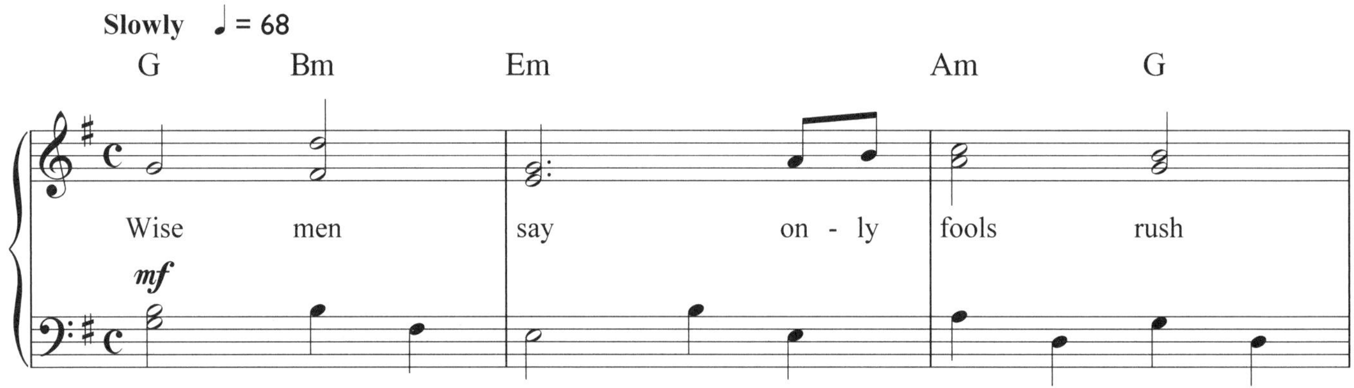

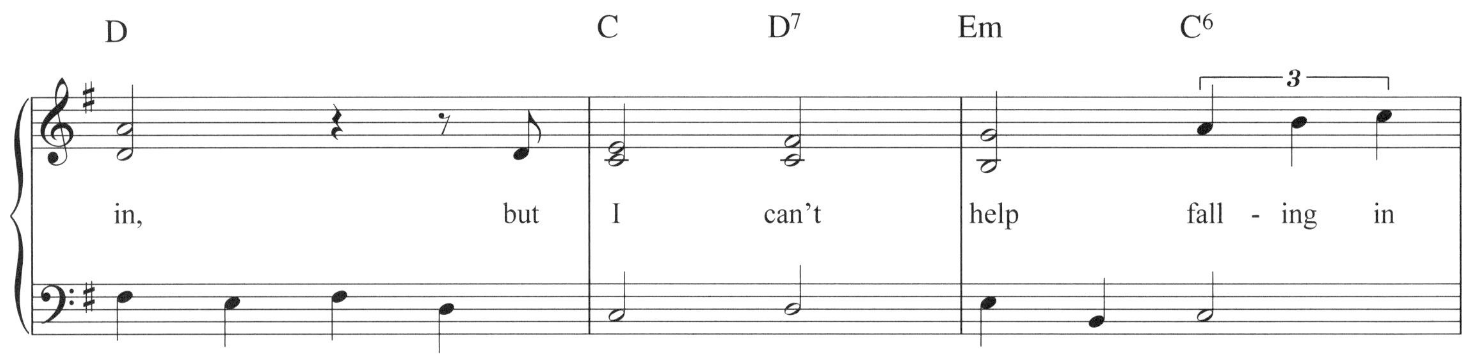

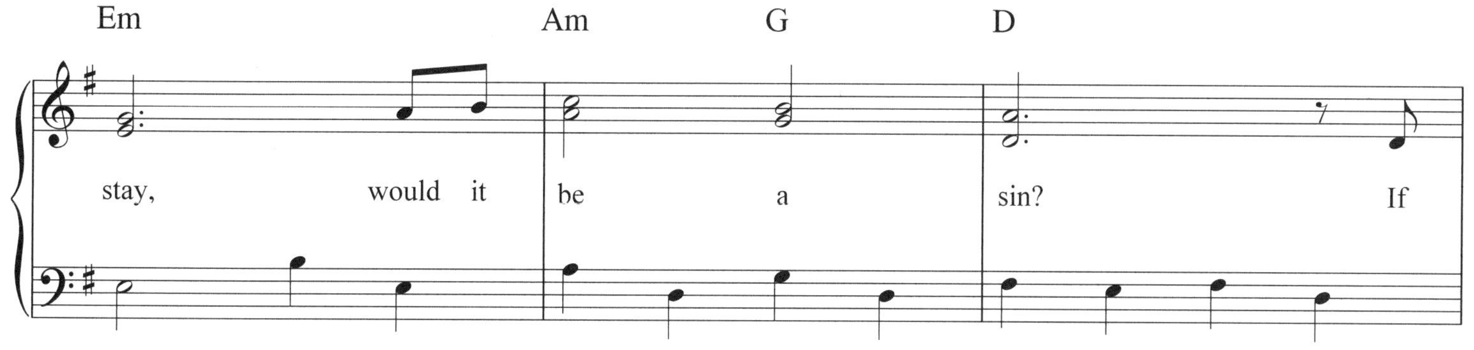
Em
Am
G
D
stay, would it be a sin? If

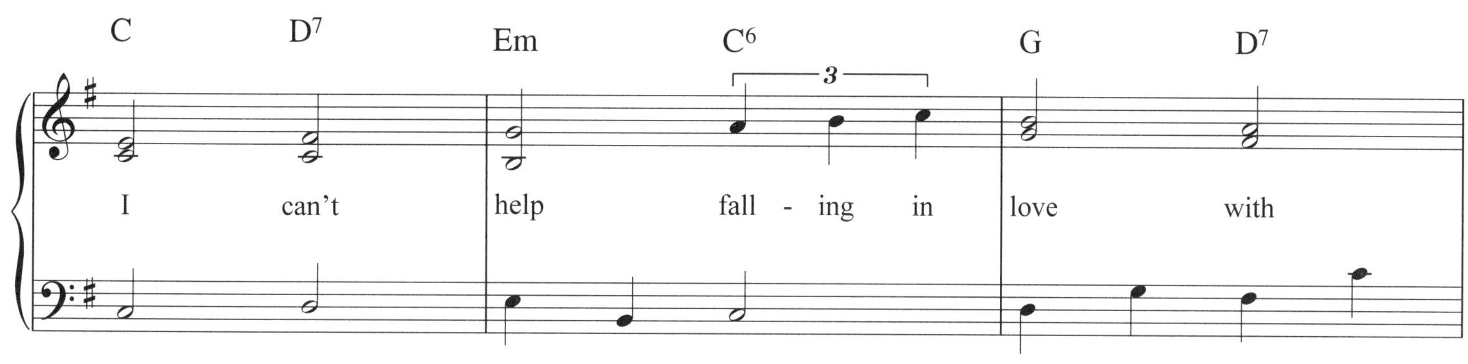
C
D7
Em
C6
3
G
D7
I can't help fall - ing in love with

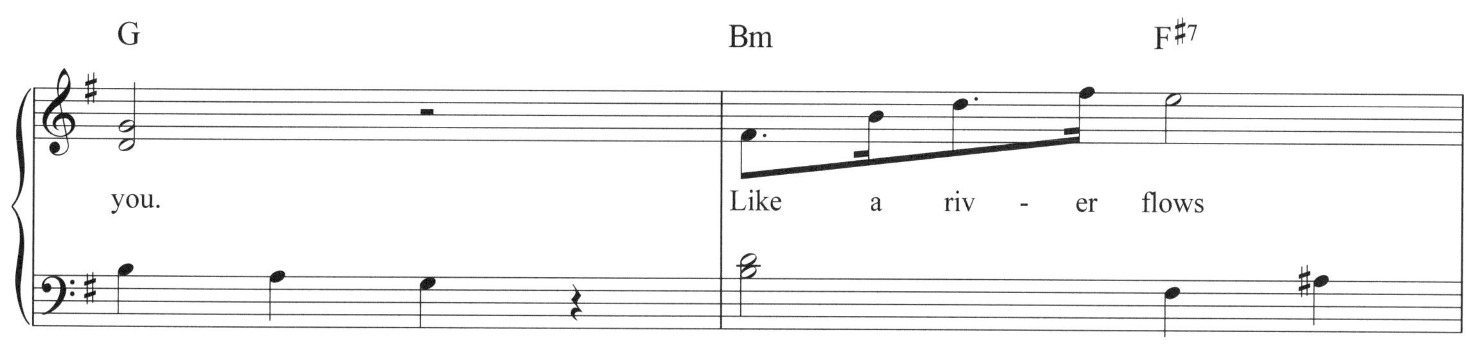
G
Bm
F♯7
you. Like a riv - er flows

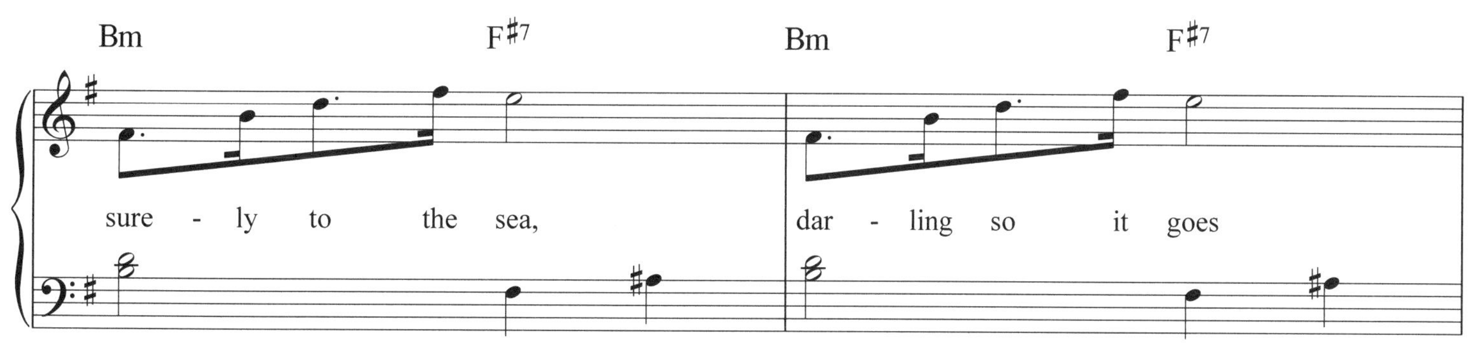
Bm
F♯7
Bm
F♯7
sure - ly to the sea, dar - ling so it goes

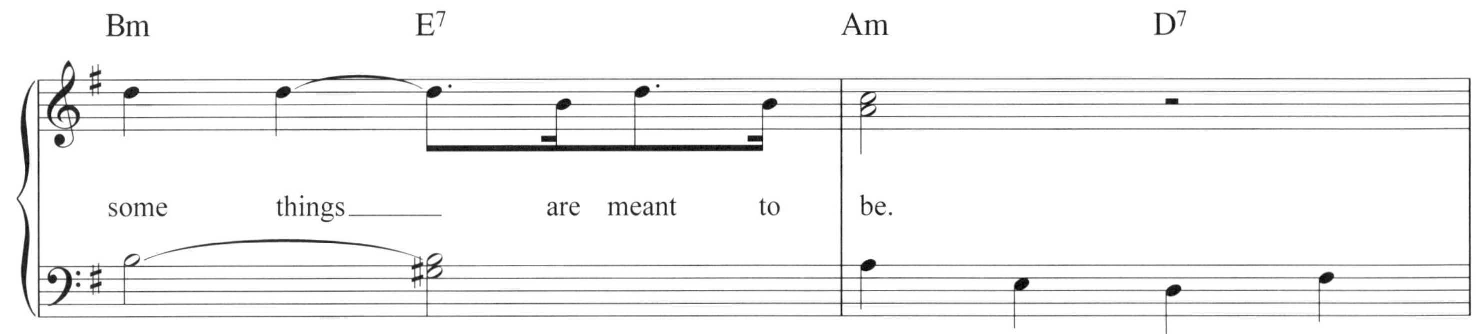
Bm
E7
Am
D7
some things are meant to be.

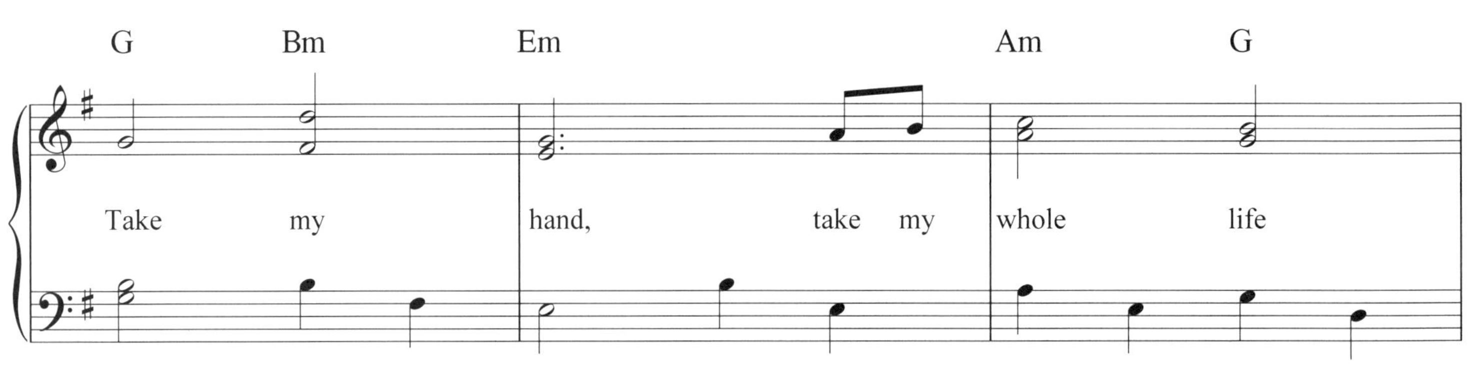
G
Bm
Em
Am
G
Take my hand, take my whole life

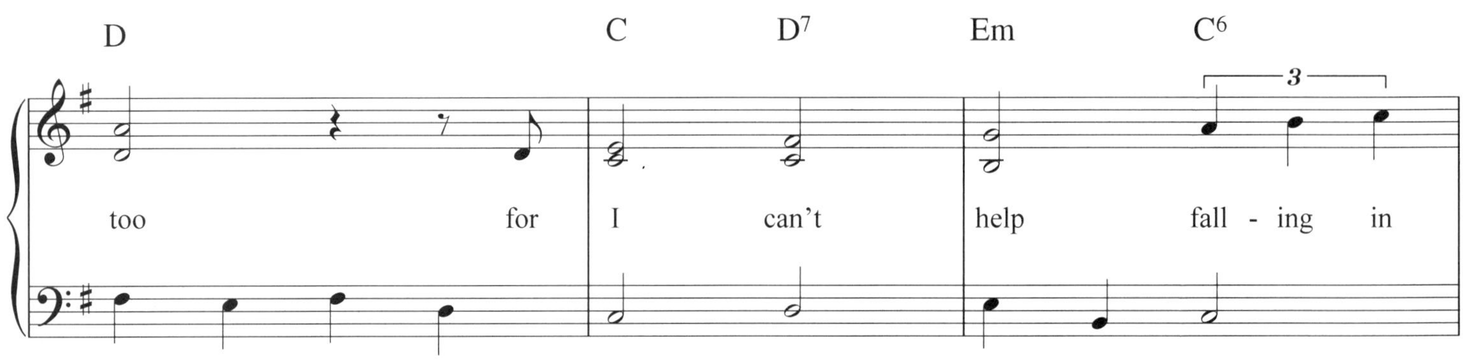
D
C
D7
Em
C6
3
too for I can't help fall - ing in

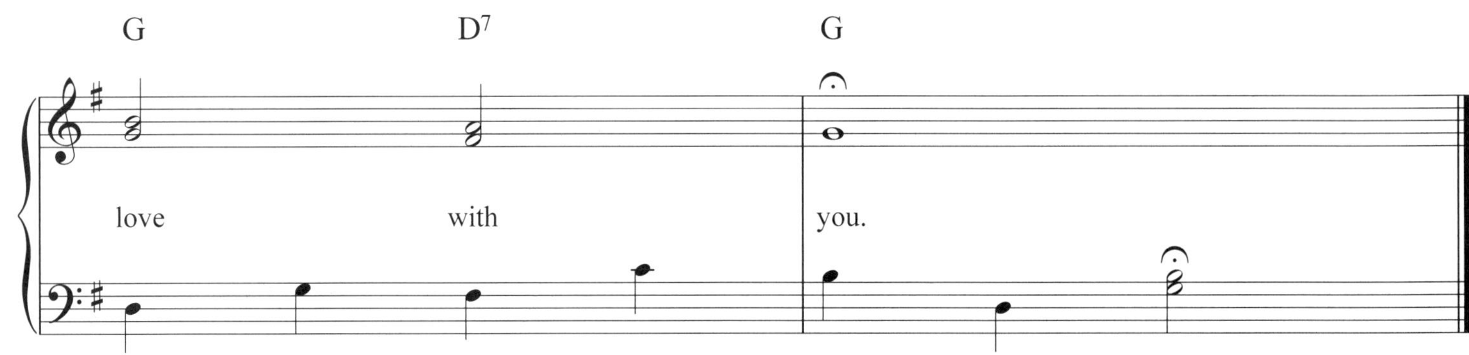
G
D7
G
love with you.

Day Tripper

Words & Music by John Lennon & Paul McCartney

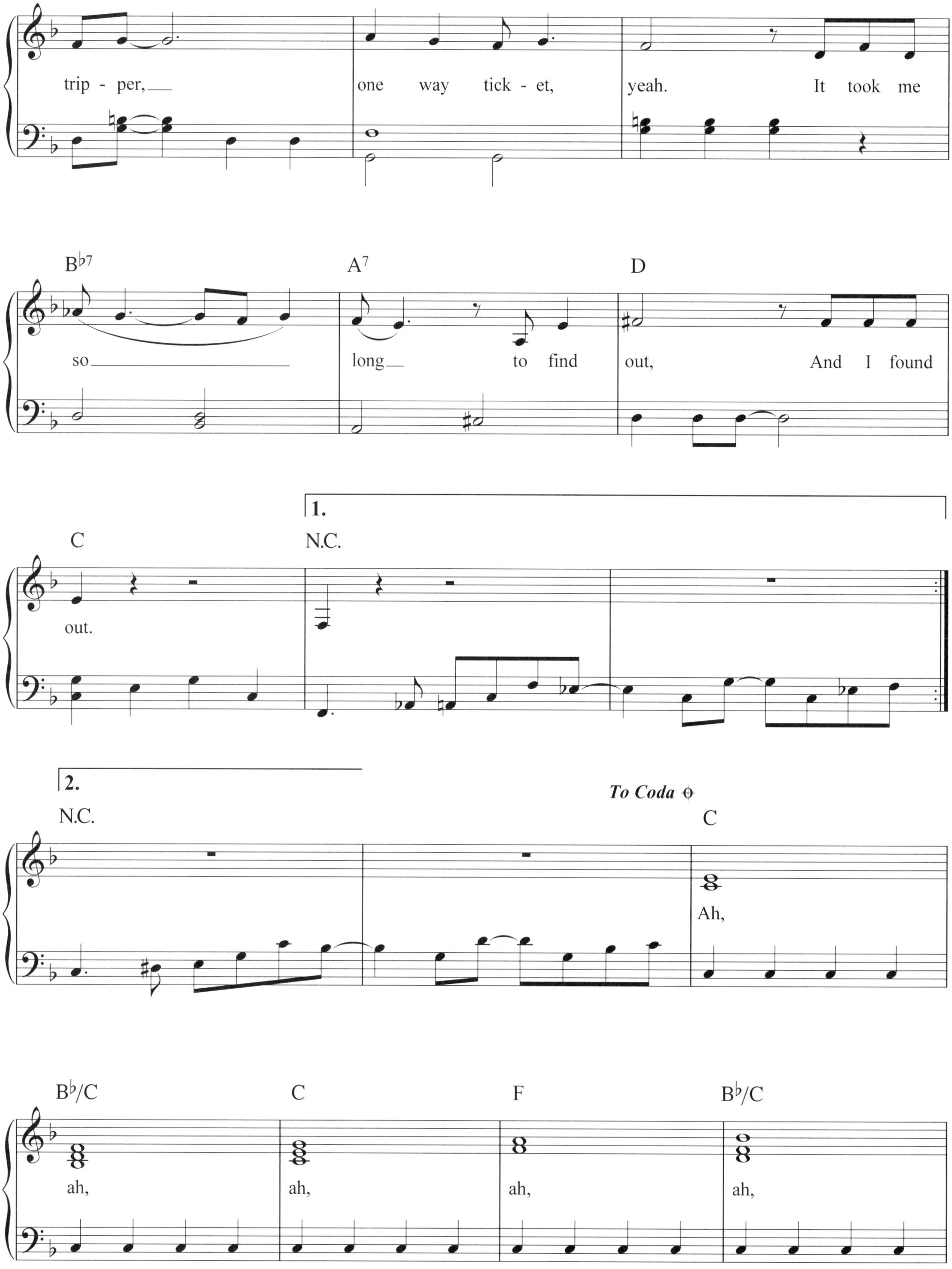

trip - per, one way tick - et, yeah. It took me

B♭7 A7 D

so long to find out, And I found

1.

C N.C.

out.

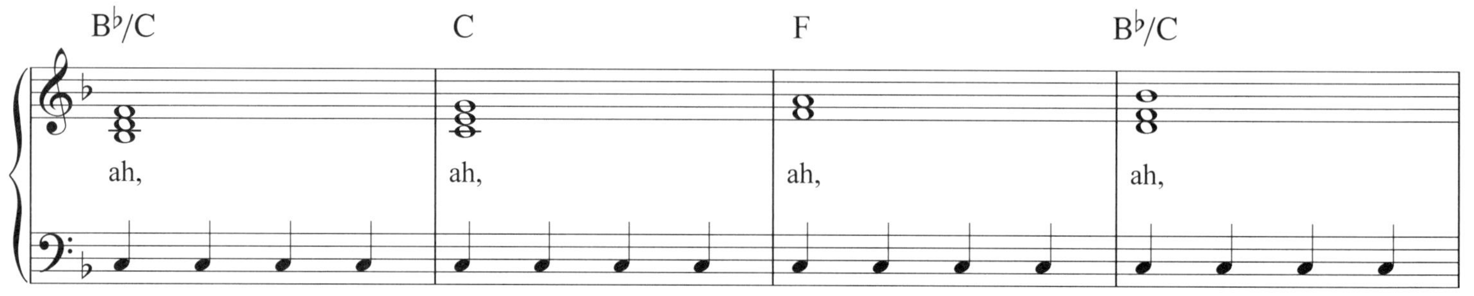

Verse 2:
She's a big teaser,
She took me half the way there.
She's a big teaser,
She took me half the way there, now.
She was a day tripper,
One way ticket, yeah!
It took me so long to find out
And I found out.

Verse 3:
Tried to please her,
She only played one night stands.
Tried to please her,
She only played one night stands, now.
She was a day tripper,
Sunday driver, yeah!
It took me so long to find out
And I found out.

Don't Cry For Me Argentina

Music by Andrew Lloyd Webber
Lyrics by Tim Rice

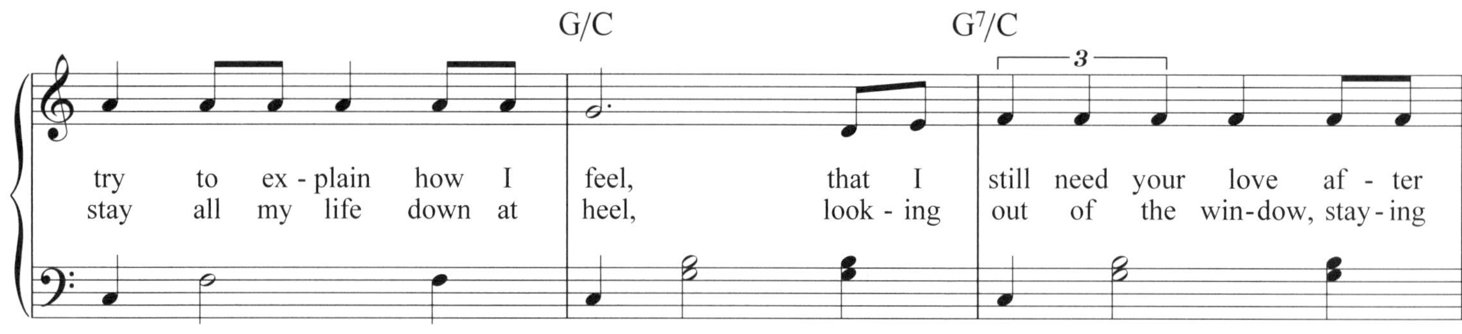

D
D7
3
All you will see is a girl you once knew, al - though she's dressed up to the
Run - ning a - round try - ing ev - 'ry - thing new, but noth - ing im - pressed me at
G
D7
G
nines, at six - es and sev - ens with you.
all. I nev - er ex - pect - ed it to.
C
F C/E C
F C
Don't cry for me Ar - gen - ti - na, the truth is I nev - er
F/A C/G C
G
Am
left you. All through my wild days, my mad ex - is - tence, I kept my
Cmaj7
F
Fmaj7
prom - ise, don't keep your dis - tance.

Every Little Thing She Does Is Magic

Words & Music by Sting

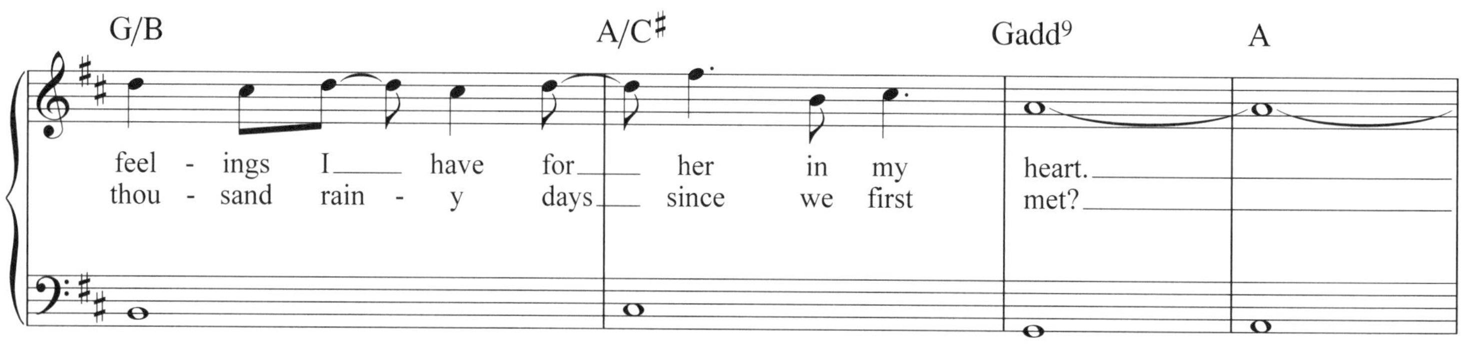

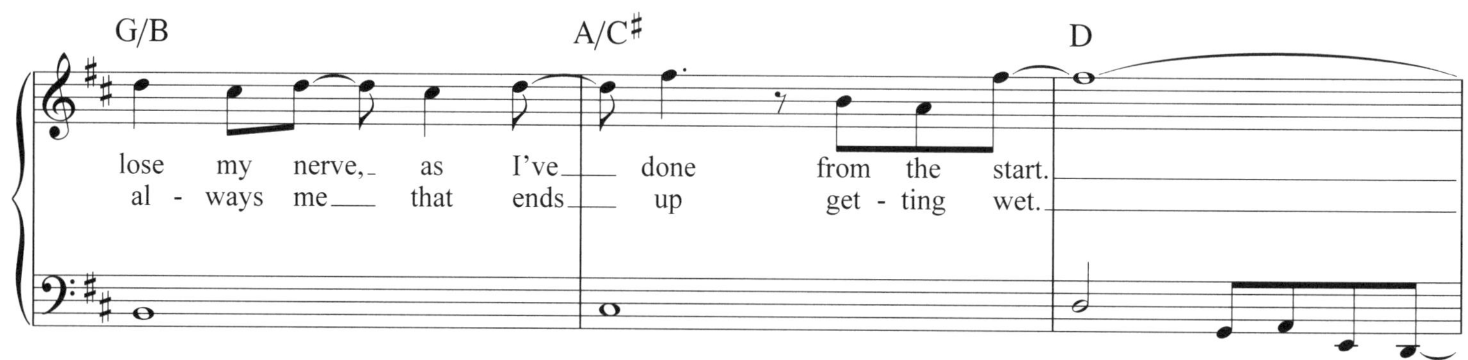

N.C.
Ev - 'ry lit - tle

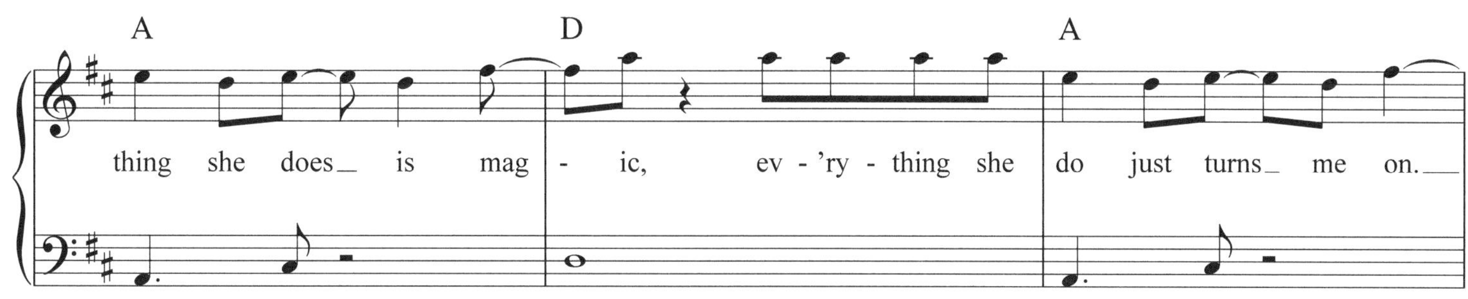
A
D
A
thing she does is mag - ic, ev - 'ry - thing she do just turns me on.

D
A
D
E - ven though my life with her was trag - ic, now I know my

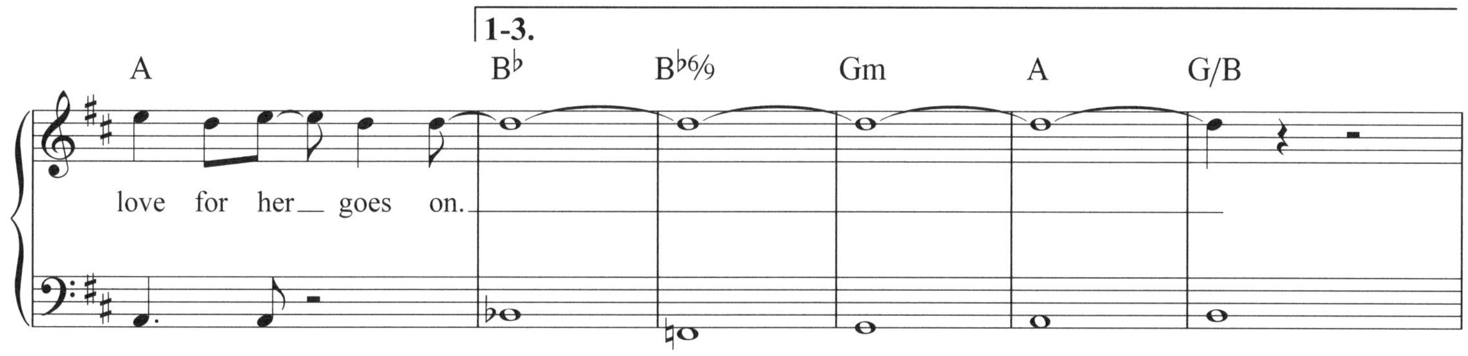
1-3.
A
B♭
B♭6/9
Gm
A
G/B
love for her goes on.

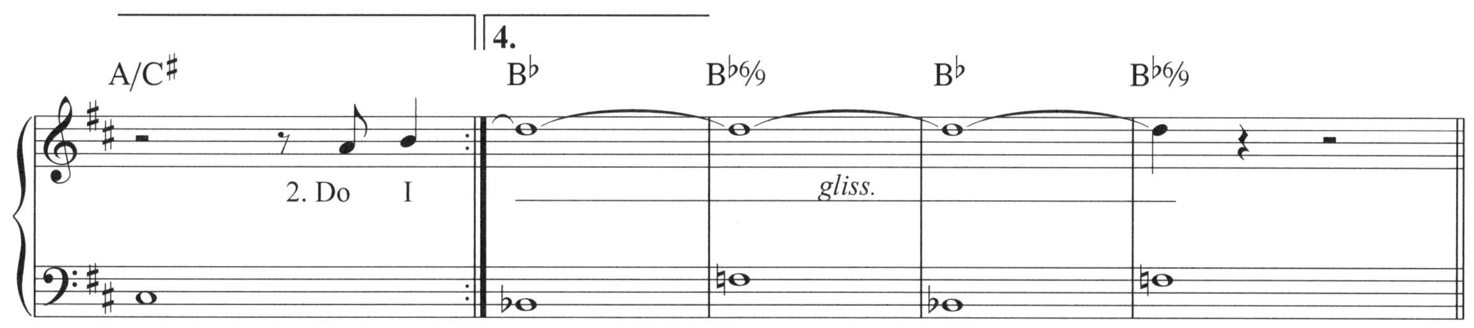
4.
A/C♯
B♭
B♭6/9
B♭
B♭6/9
2. Do I
gliss.

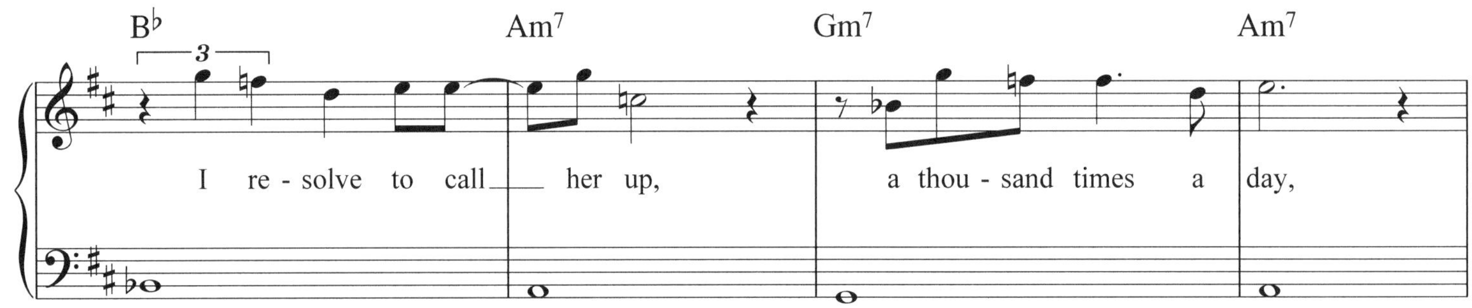
B♭
Am7
Gm7
Am7
3
I re - solve to call her up,
a thou - sand times a day,

Gm7
Am7
B♭
and ask her if she'll mar - ry me
in some old - fash - ioned way.

Am7
B♭
Cadd9
3
But my si - lent fears have gripped me long be - fore

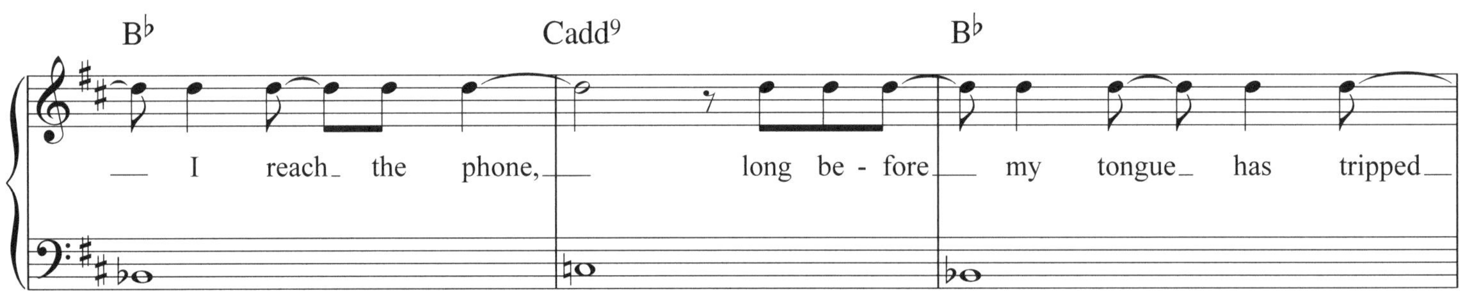
B♭
Cadd9
B♭
I reach the phone, long be - fore my tongue has tripped

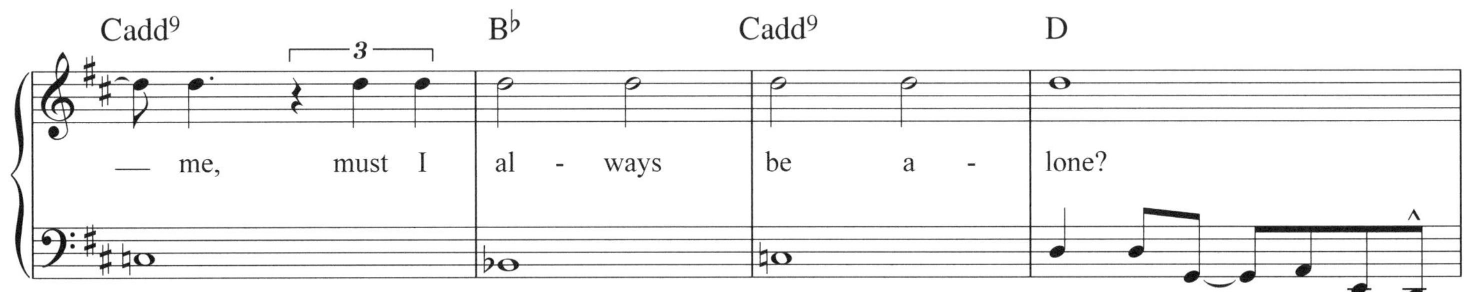
Cadd9
B♭
Cadd9
D
3
me, must I al - ways be a - lone?

N.C.
A
D
Ev - 'ry lit - tle
thing she does is mag - ic, ev - 'ry - thing she

A
D
A
do just turns me on.
E - ven though my
life with her was trag -

D
A
1.
D
- ic, now I know my
love for her goes on.
Ev - 'ry lit - tle

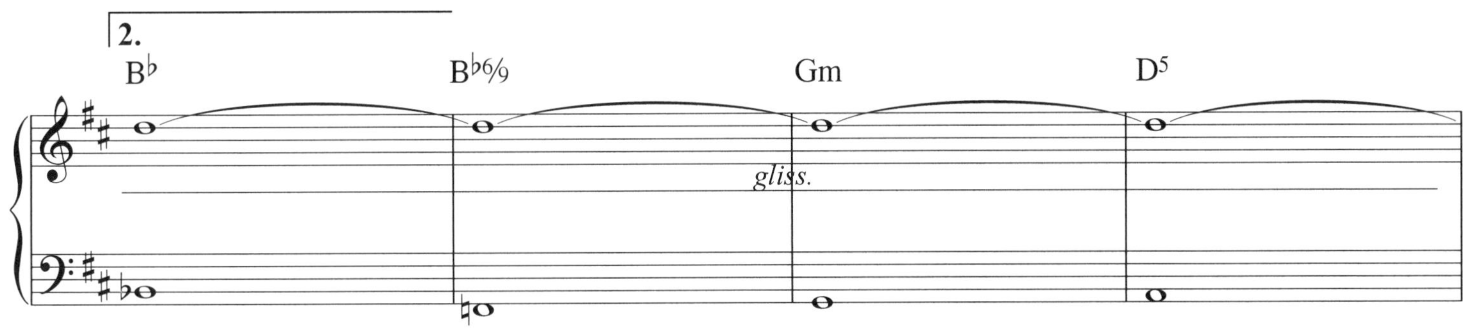
2.
B♭
B♭6/9
Gm
D5
gliss.

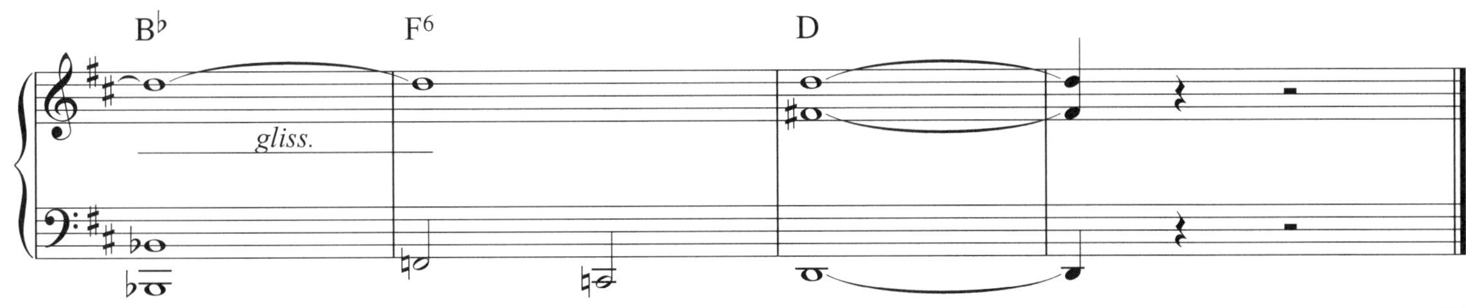
B♭
F6
D
gliss.

God Only Knows

Words & Music by Brian Wilson & Tony Asher

A
D
Gm
3
on, be - lieve me,
the world could show
noth - ing to me,

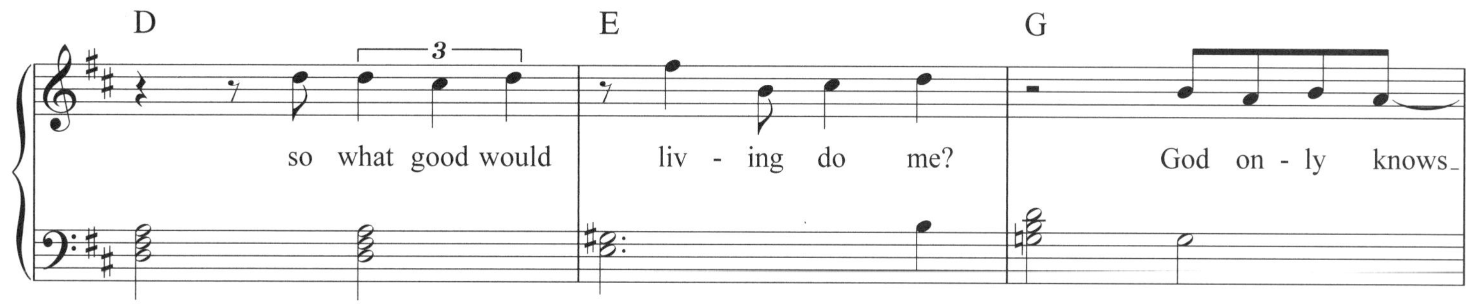
D
E
G
3
so what good would
liv - ing do me?
God on - ly knows

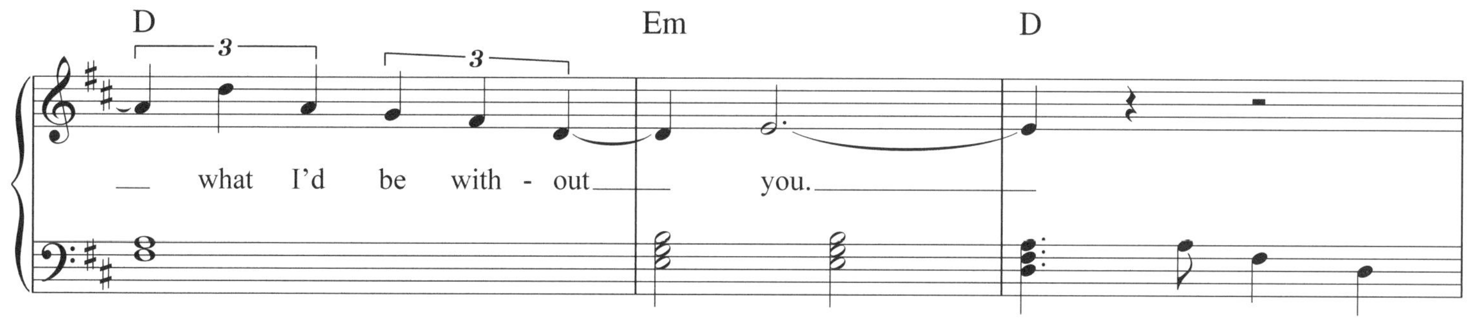
D
Em
D
3
3
what I'd be with - out
you.

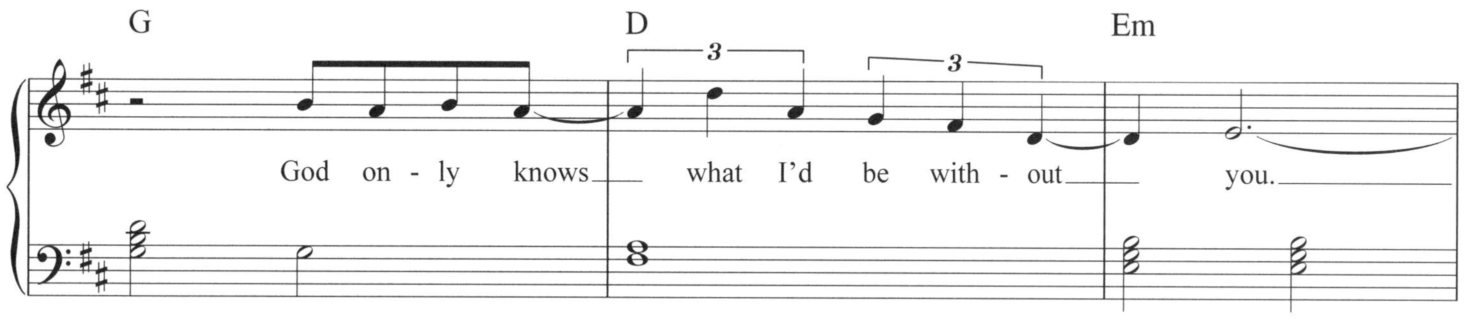
G
D
Em
3
3
God on - ly knows
what I'd be with - out
you.

D
G
N.C.
D
God on - ly knows.

Hallelujah

Words & Music by Leonard Cohen

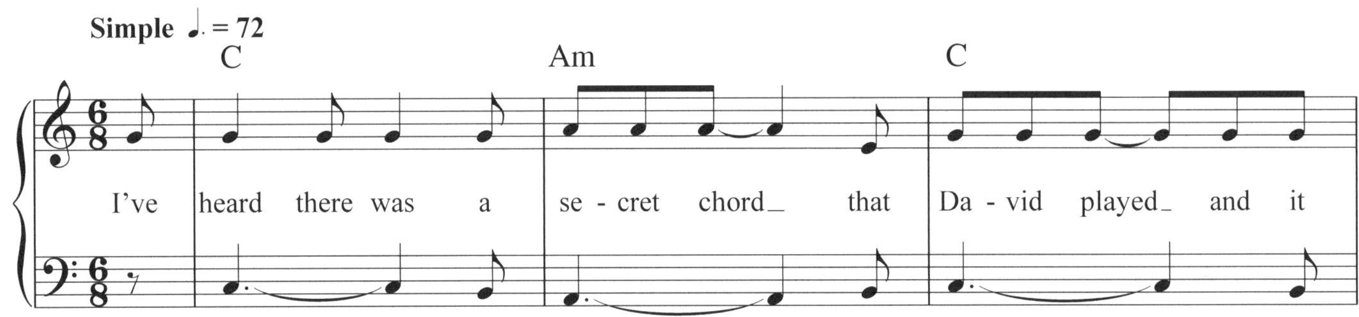

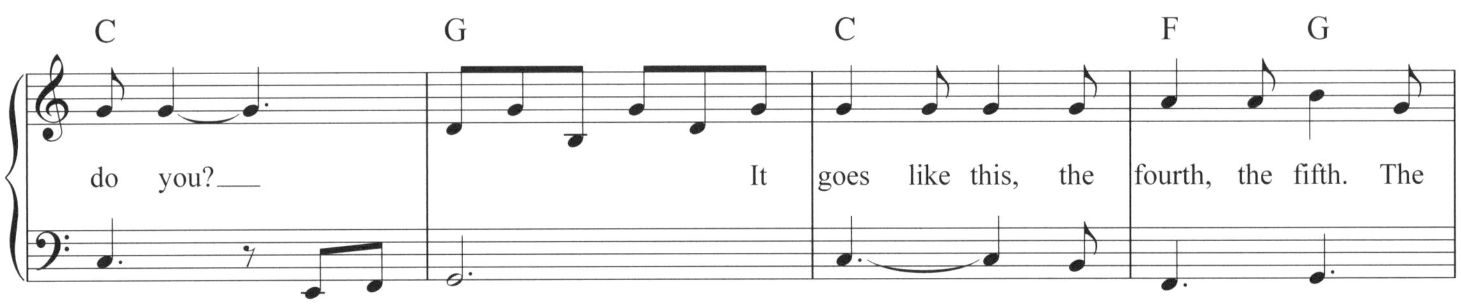

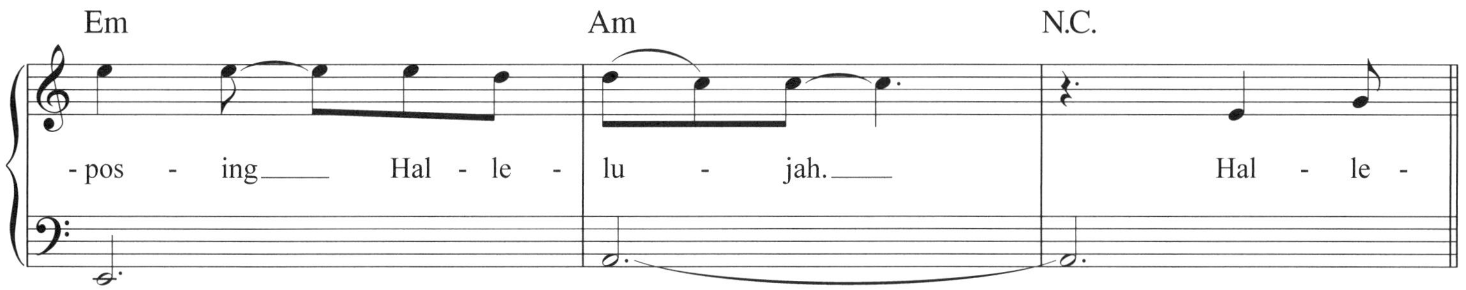
Em
Am
N.C.
-pos - ing Hal - le - lu - jah. Hal - le -

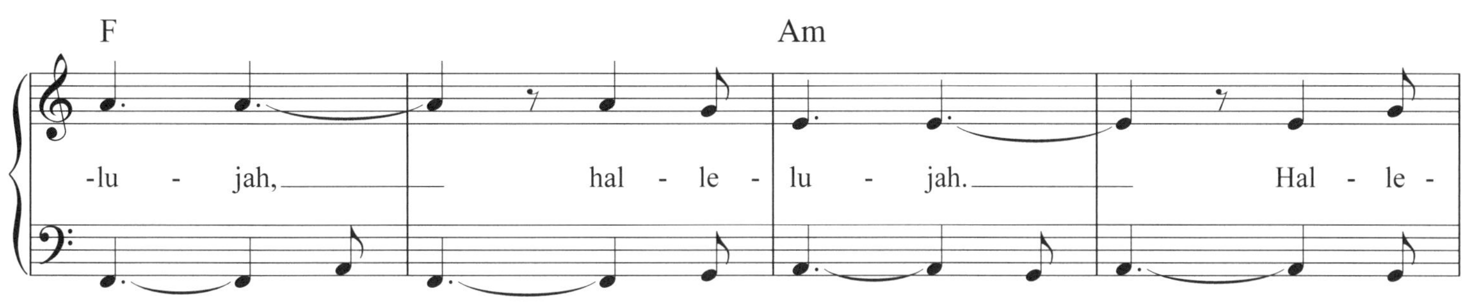
F
Am
-lu - jah, hal - le - lu - jah. Hal - le -

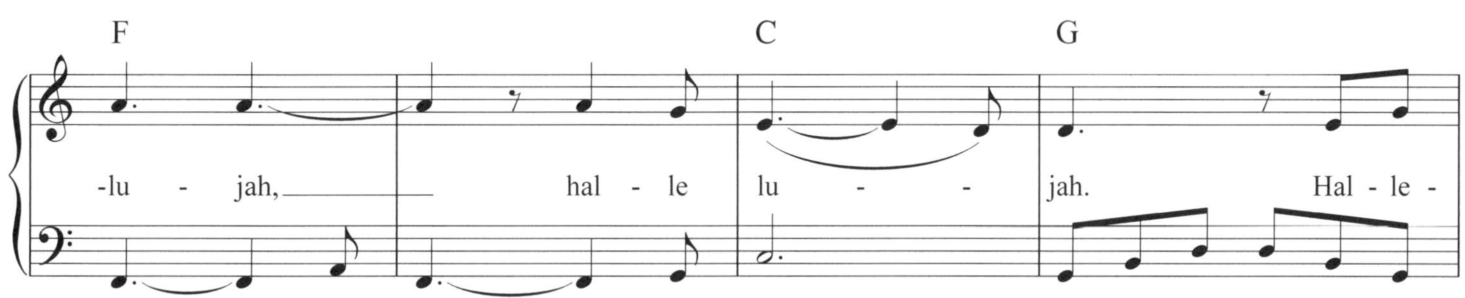
F
C
G
-lu - jah, hal - le lu - - jah. Hal - le -

F
Am
F
-lu - jah, hal - le - lu - jah. Hal - le lu - jah,

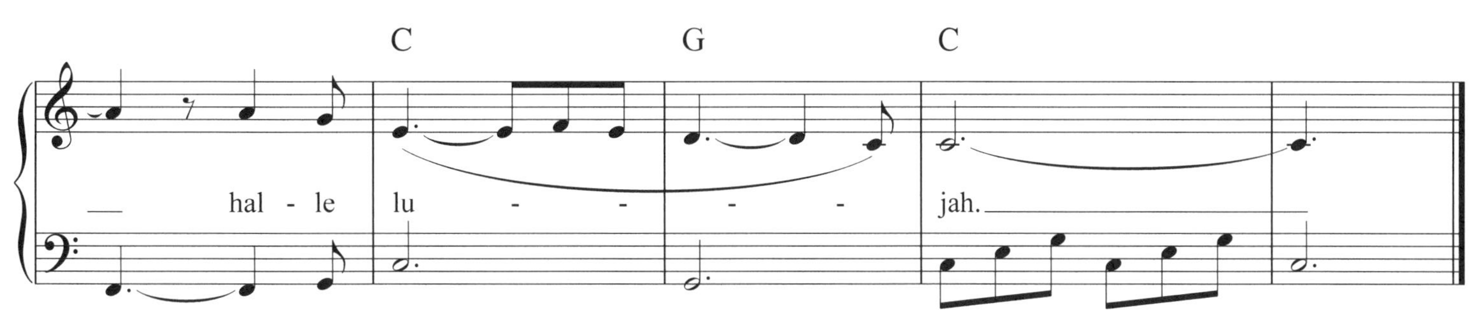
C
G
C
hal - le lu - - - - jah.

Heartbeat

Words & Music by Bob Montgomery & Norman Petty

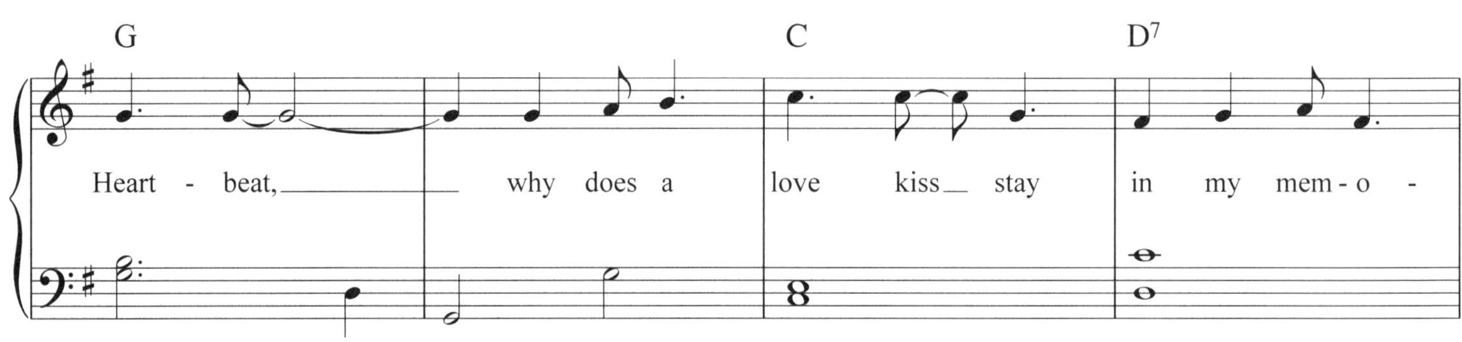

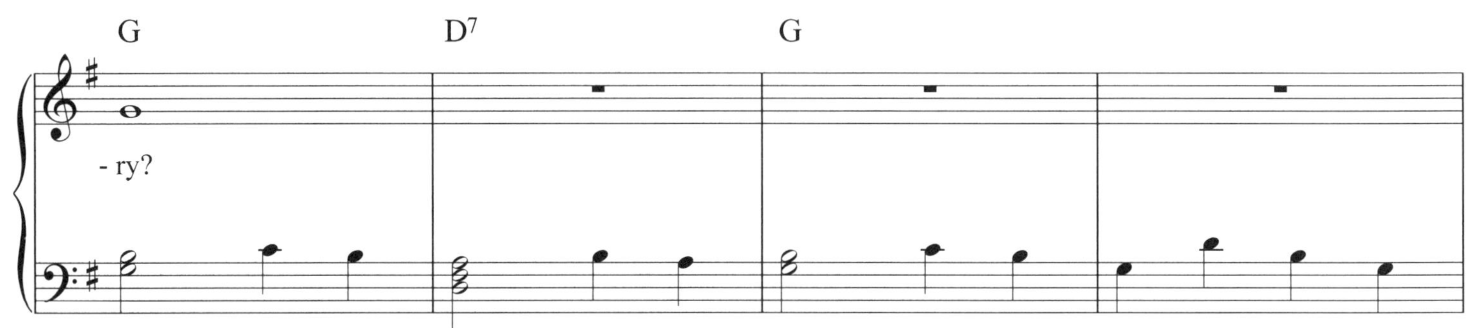

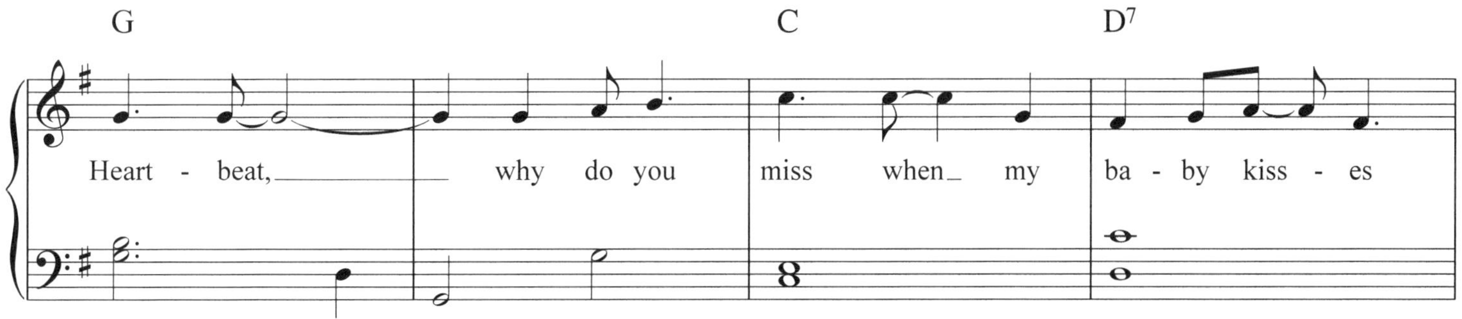

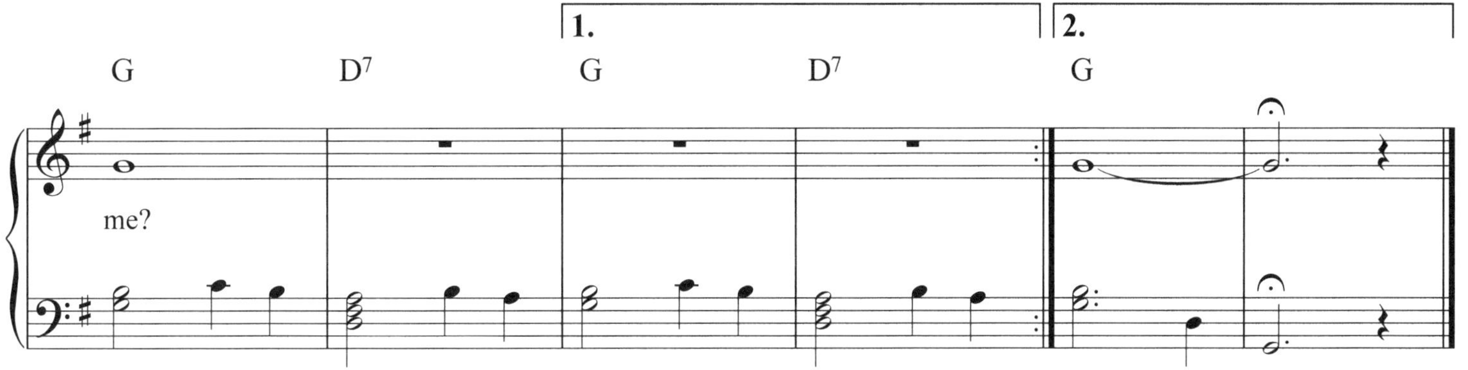

Verse 2:
Heartbeat, why do you skip when my baby's lips meet mine?
Heartbeat, why do you flip, then give me a skip-beat sign?
Riddledeepat, and sing to me love's story, and bring to me love's glory.
Heartbeat why do you miss when my baby kisses me?

Hero

Words & Music by Mariah Carey & Walter Afanasieff

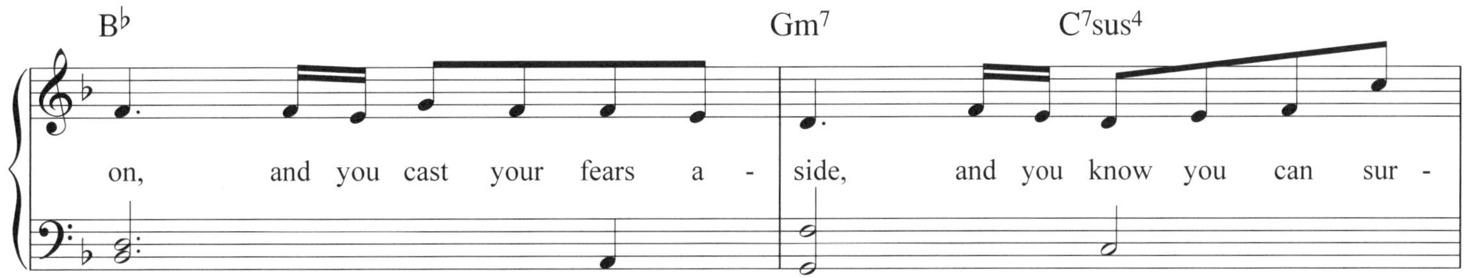
B♭
Gm7
C7sus4
on, and you cast your fears a - side, and you know you can sur -

F
Dm
- vive. So when you feel like hope is gone, look in - side you and be

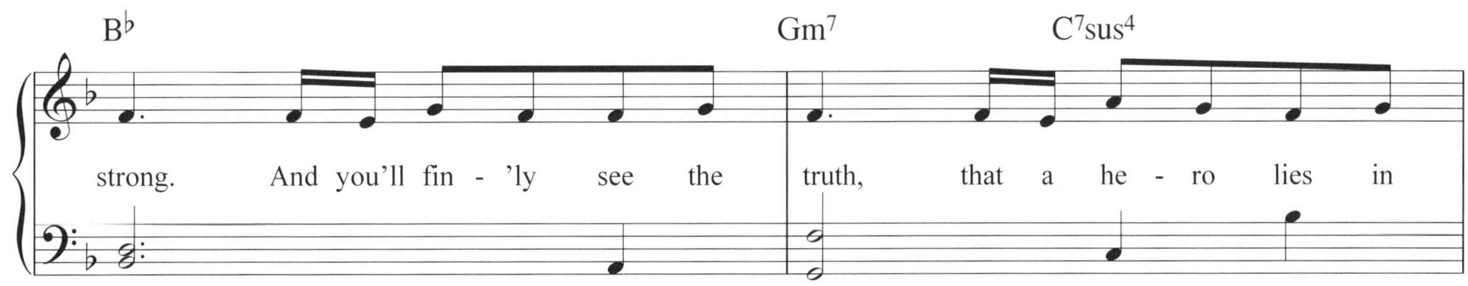
B♭
Gm7
C7sus4
strong. And you'll fin - 'ly see the truth, that a he - ro lies in

F
Gm7
C7sus4
you, that a he - ro lies in

B♭
B♭/A
Gm7
C7
F
you, that a he - ro lies in you.

Innocent Eyes

Words & Music by Delta Goodrem & Vince Pizzanga

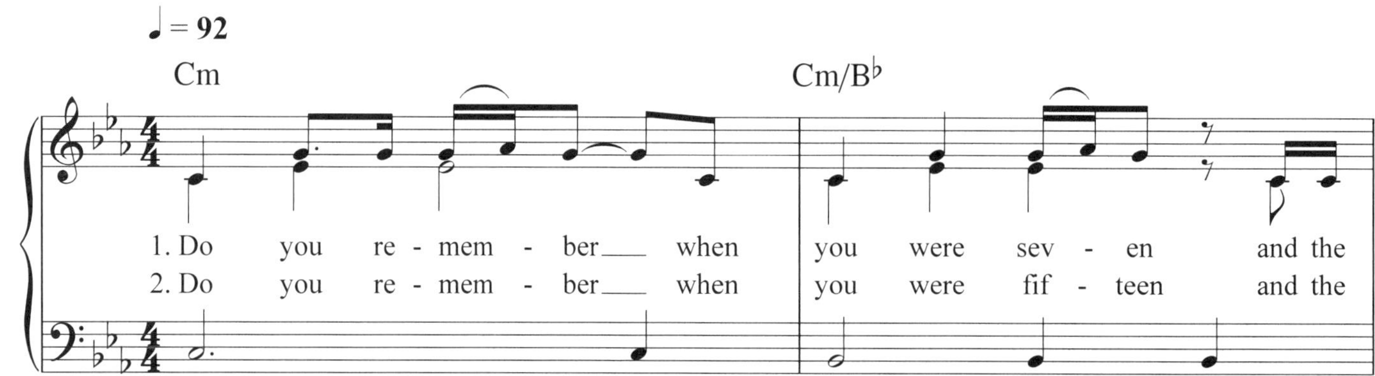

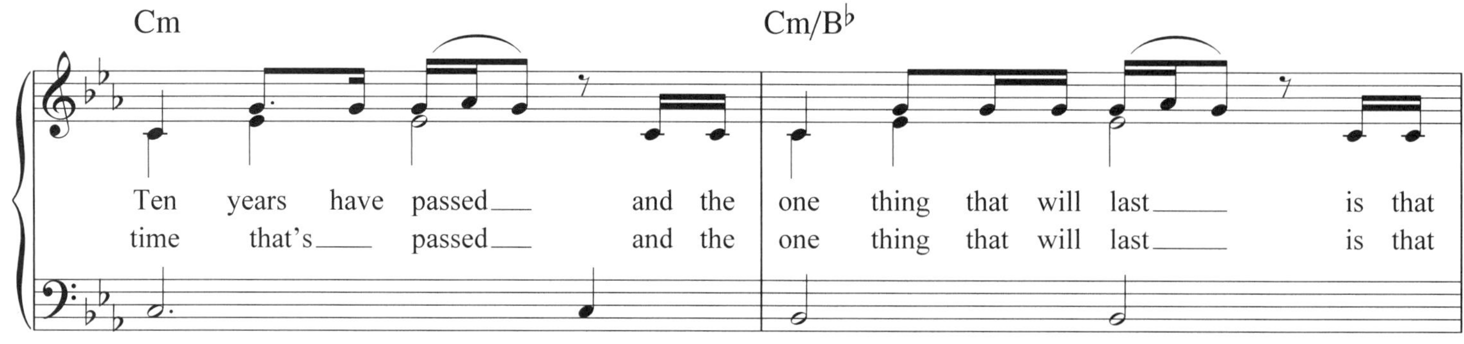

A♭
G
same old song that we played a - long and made my mam - ma cry.
same old song that we played a - long and made my dad - dy cry.
Bm
Gmaj7
F♯
I miss those days and I miss those ways when
Bm
Gmaj7
F♯
I got lost in fan - ta - sies, in a car - toon land of mys - te - ries, in a
place you won't grow old, in a place you won't feel cold, and I'll sing...
Bm
G
A
F♯sus4
(Da da da da da da da da da da da da.) Seems I'm lost in my re -

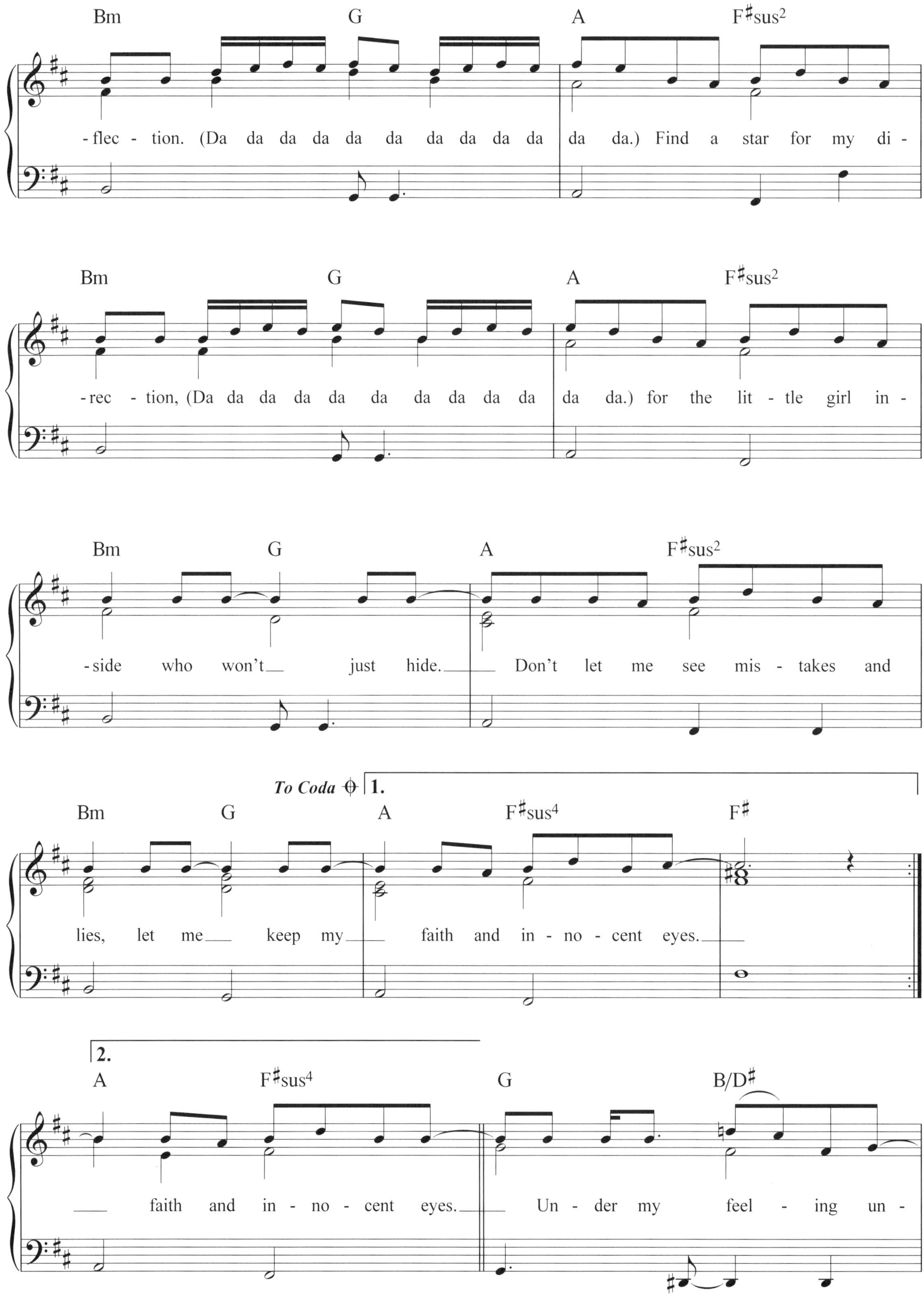

Bm G A F♯sus2

-flec - tion. (Da da da da da da da da da da da da.) Find a star for my di -

Bm G A F♯sus2

-rec - tion, (Da da da da da da da da da da da da.) for the lit - tle girl in -

Bm G A F♯sus2

-side who won't just hide. Don't let me see mis - takes and

To Coda 𝄌

Em
F♯
G
B/D♯
- der my skin, under the thoughts from
Em
F♯
G
B/D♯
within, learning the subtext of
Em
G
B/D♯
the mind. See creation how
D.S. al Coda
Em
F♯
Bm
F♯
we're defined, in my innocent eyes.
Coda
A
F♯sus4
Bm
G
faith and innocent eyes. (Da da da da da da da da da da

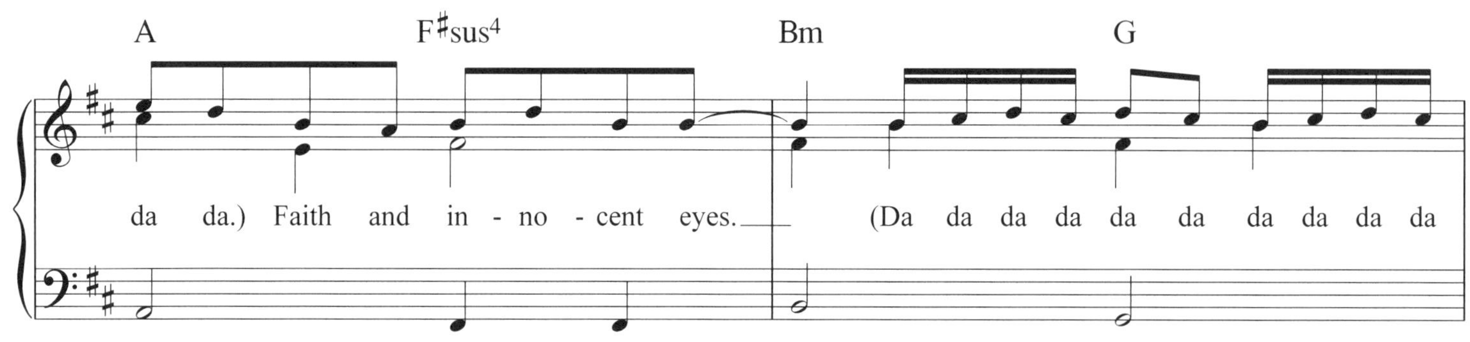
A F♯sus4 Bm G
da da.) Faith and in - no - cent eyes.
(Da da da da da da da da da da

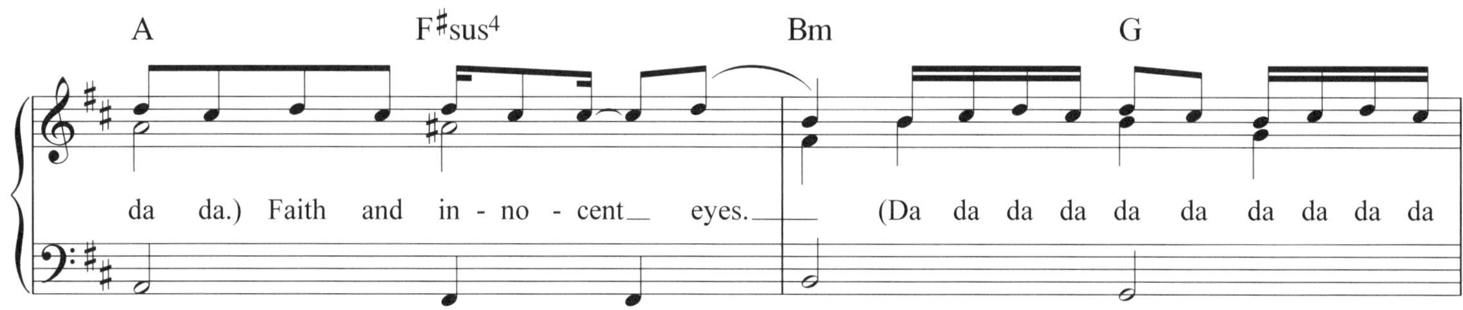
A F♯sus4 Bm G
da da.) Faith and in - no - cent eyes.
(Da da da da da da da da da da

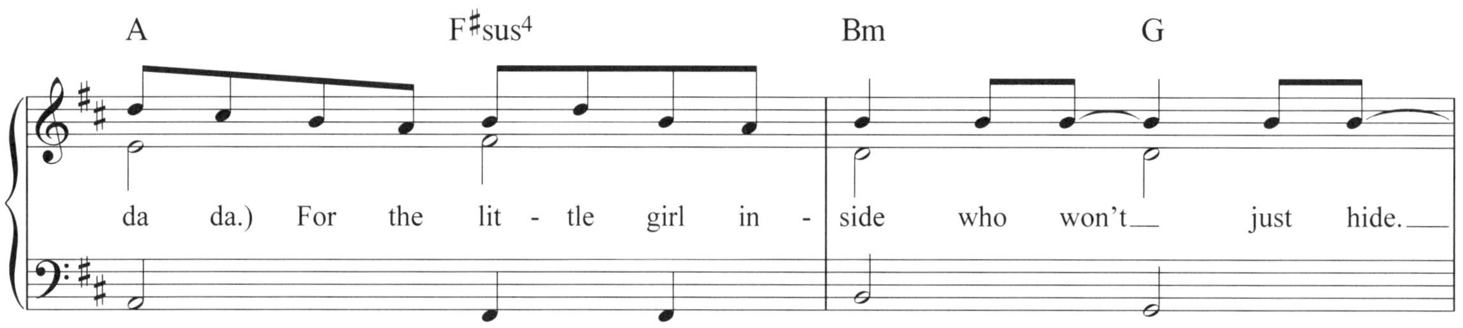
A F♯sus4 Bm G
da da.) For the lit - tle girl in - side who won't just hide.

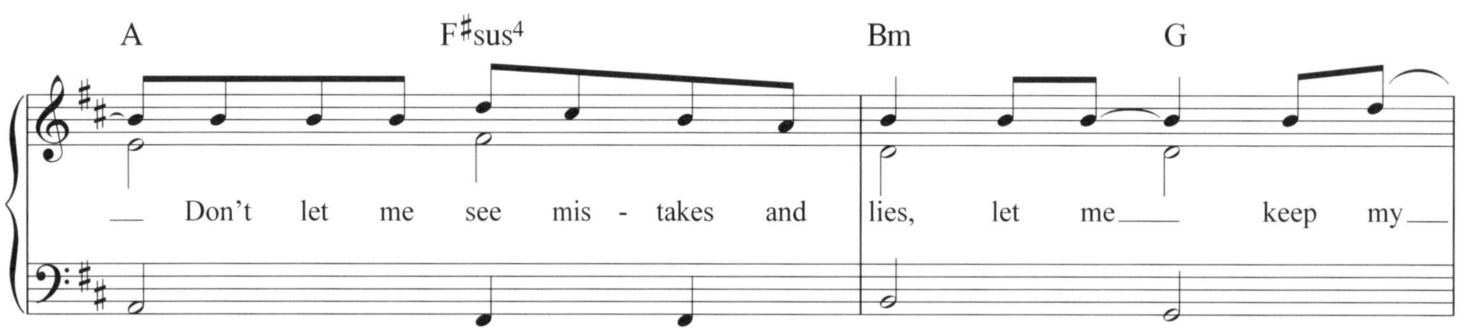
A F♯sus4 Bm G
Don't let me see mis - takes and lies, let me keep my

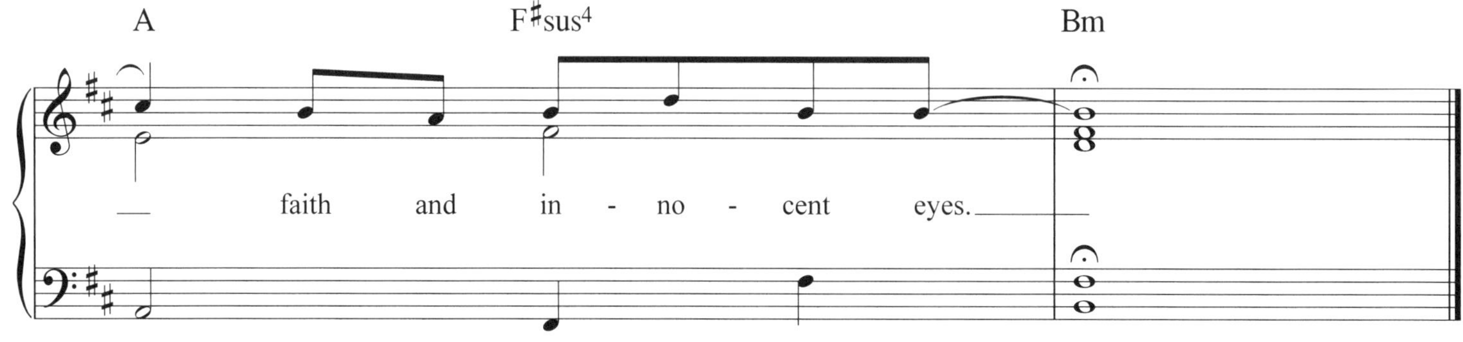
A F♯sus4 Bm
faith and in - no - cent eyes.

The Lady In Red

Words & Music by Chris De Burgh

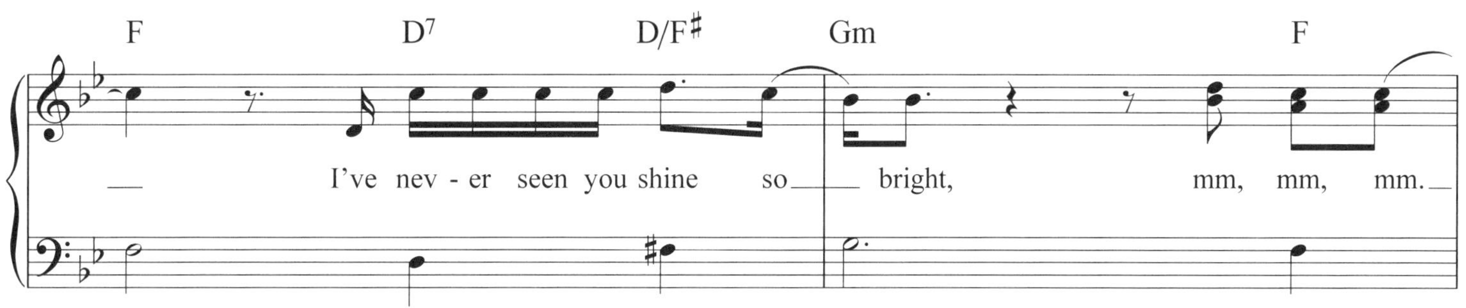

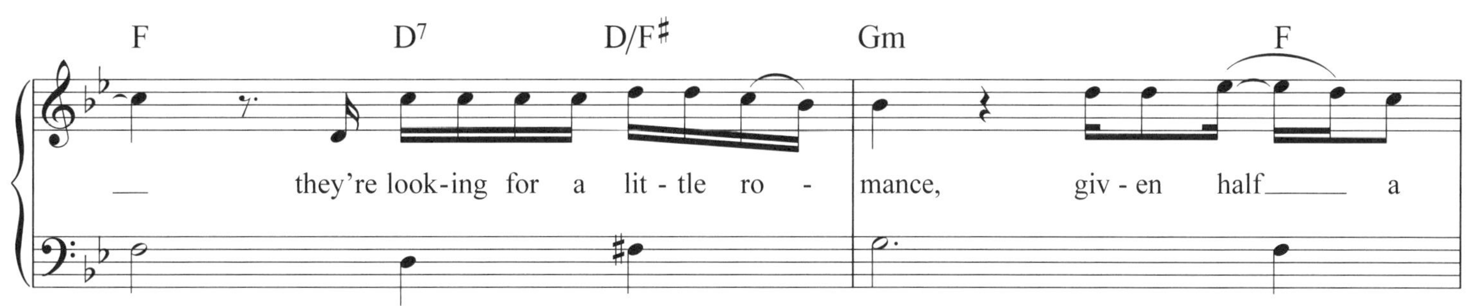

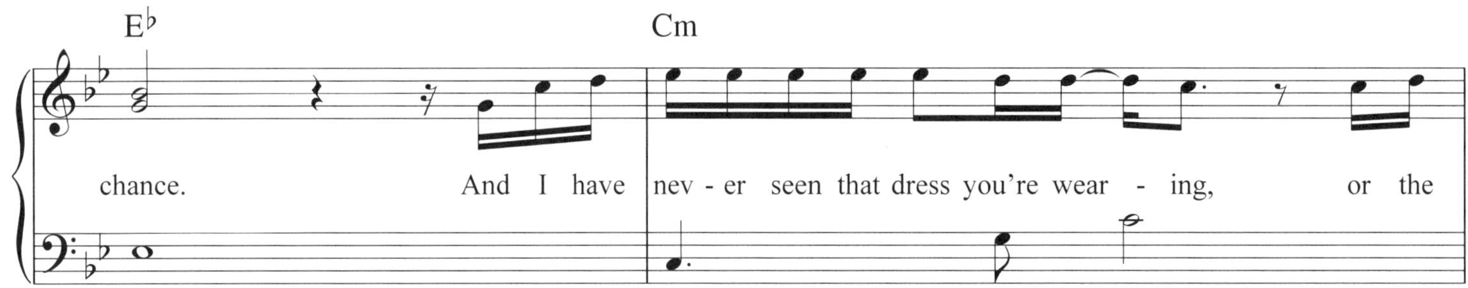
E♭
Cm
chance. And I have nev - er seen that dress you're wear - ing, or the

Gm
high-lights in your hair that catch your eyes; I have been

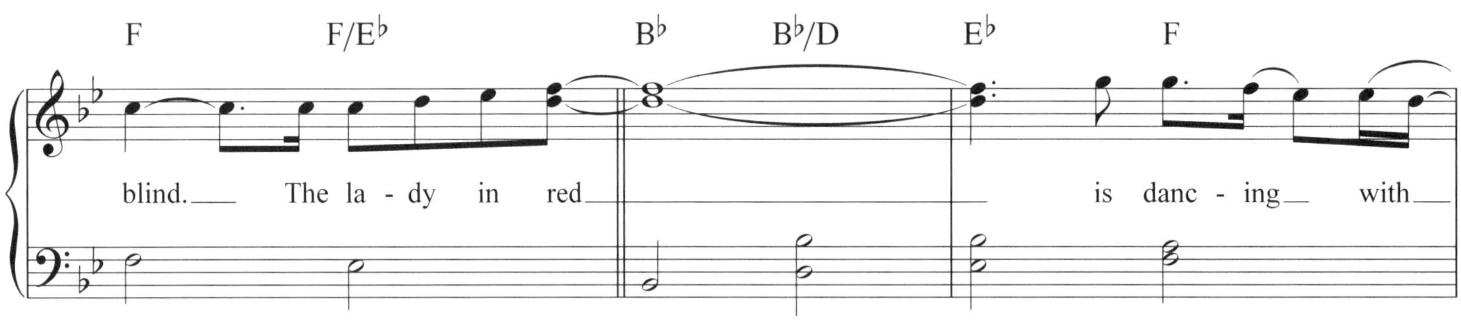
F
F/E♭
B♭
B♭/D
E♭
F
blind. The la - dy in red is danc - ing with

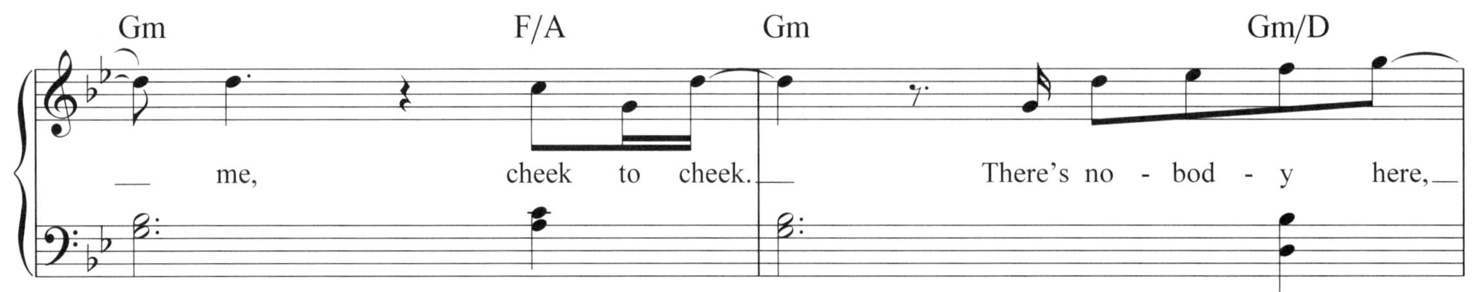
Gm
F/A
Gm
Gm/D
me, cheek to cheek. There's no - bod - y here,

Cm7
F
B♭
it's just you and me.
It's where I want to be.
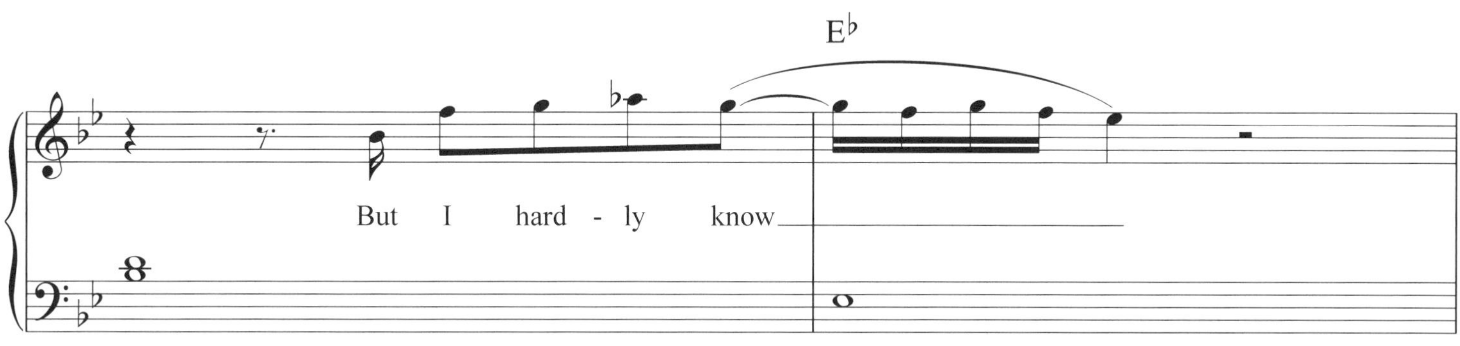
E♭
But I hard - ly know
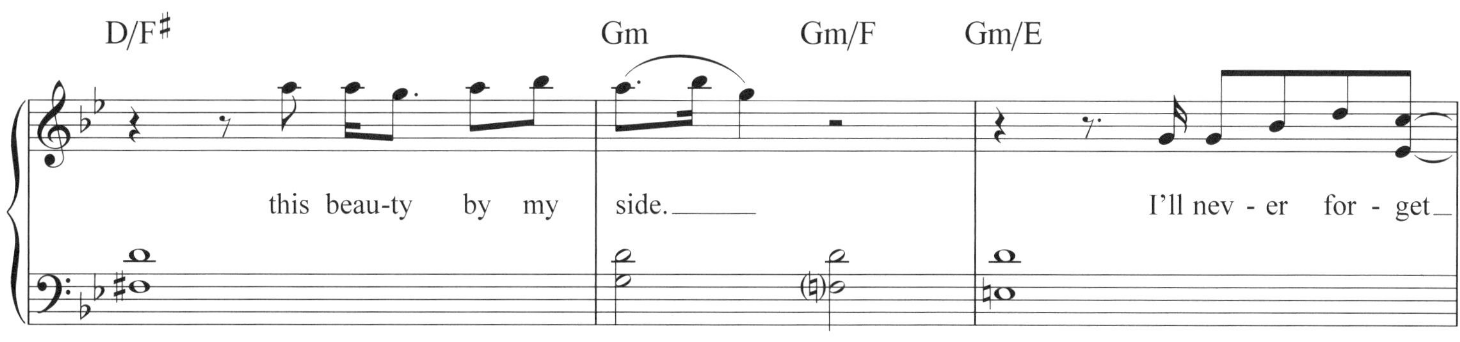
D/F♯
Gm
Gm/F
Gm/E
this beau-ty by my side.
I'll nev - er for - get

Cm
F
B♭
the way you look to - night.

A Little Time

Words & Music by Paul Heaton & David Rotheray

B♭
C
B♭
has - n't it, has - n't it?
won't you, won't you?
do you, do you? The
Prom - is - es, prom - is - es,
Lips that prom - ise,
free - dom that you
C
F
Gm
turn to dust;
fear the worst.
want - ed back is
wed - ding bells just
Tongue so sharp the
yours for good; I
turn to rust,
bub - ble burst.
hope you're glad.
To Coda
1.
2.
B♭/D
C/E
C/E
trust in - to mis -
Just in - to un -
Sad in - to un -
trust.
(M) 2. I need a lit - tle
- just.
F
N.C.
D.S. al Coda
(M) 3. I've had a lit - tle

𝄌 *Coda*

C/E
N.C.
F
-sad.
I had a lit-tle
time to think it
o - ver.
Had a lit-tle

room to work it
out.
I found a lit-tle
cou - rage to call it

off.
I've had a lit-tle
time.
I've had a lit-tle

time.
I've had a lit-tle
time.

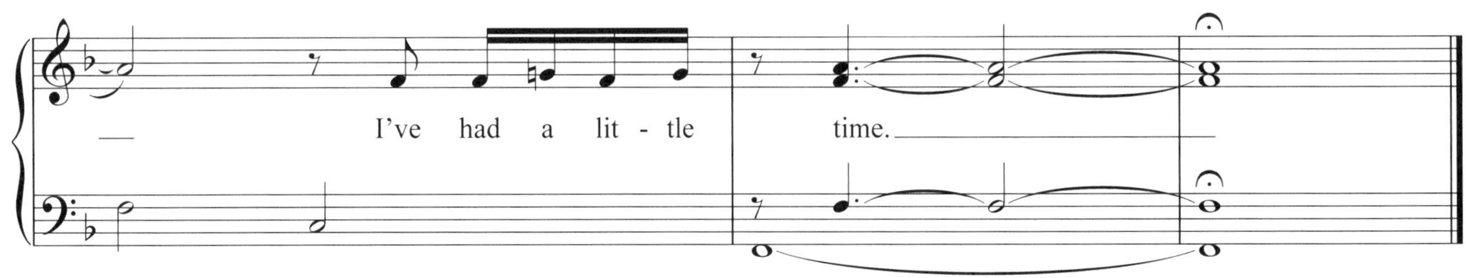
I've had a lit - tle
time.

A Thousand Miles

Words & Music by Vanessa Carlton

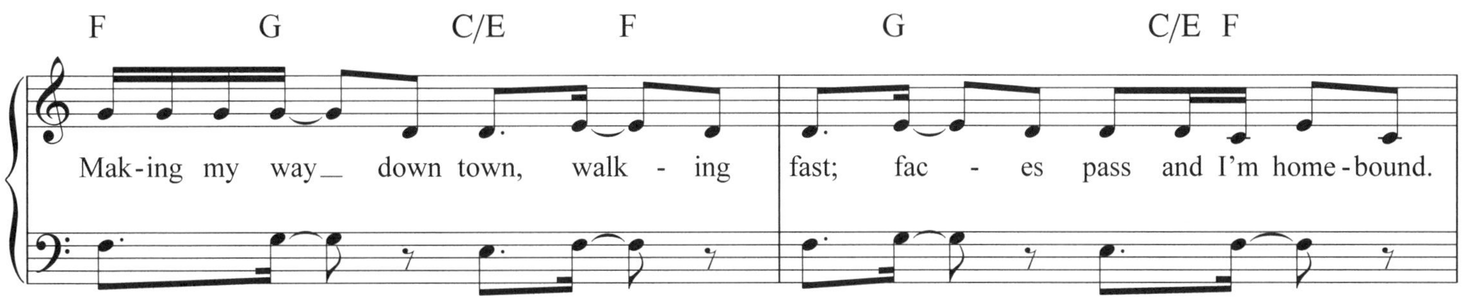

G
C/E
F
G
C/E
F
Star - ing blan - kly a - head, just mak - ing my
way, just mak - ing a way through_ the

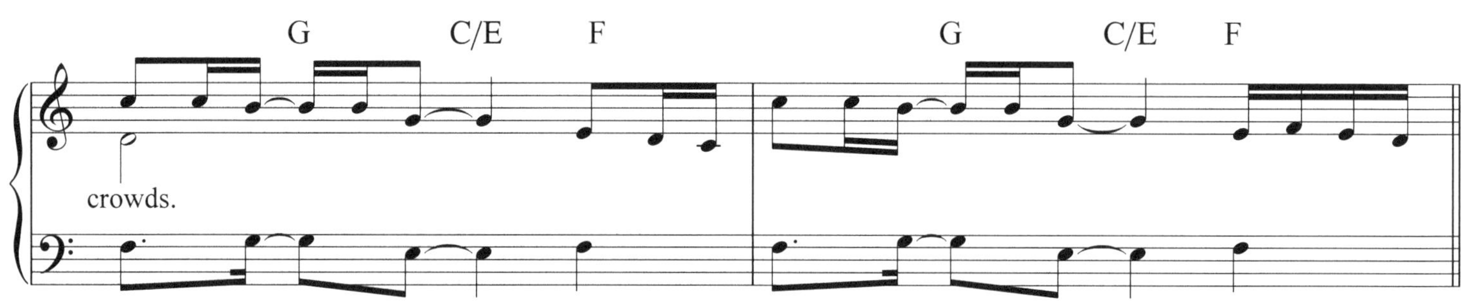
G
C/E
F
G
C/E
F
crowds.

F
C/G
Em
F
C/G
Em
I still need you,_
I still miss you,

F
C/G
Em
F
G
and now I
won - der: If

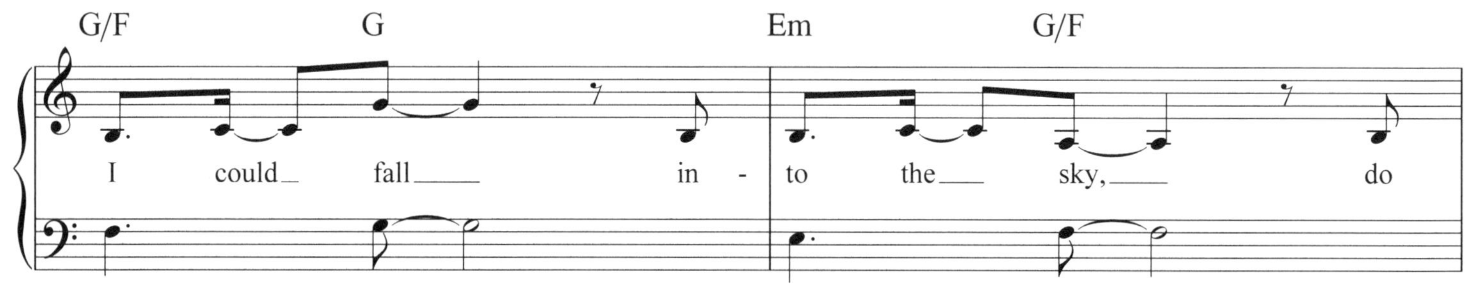
G/F
G
Em
G/F
I could_ fall___ in -
to the___ sky,___ do

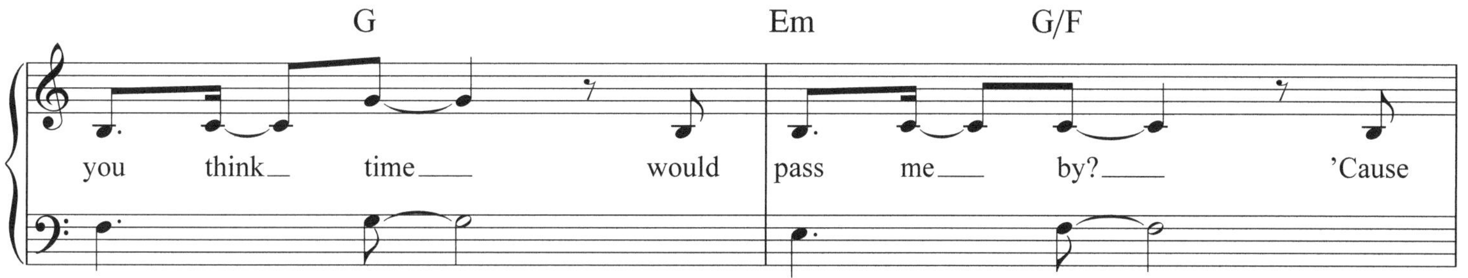
G
Em
G/F
you think time would pass me by? 'Cause

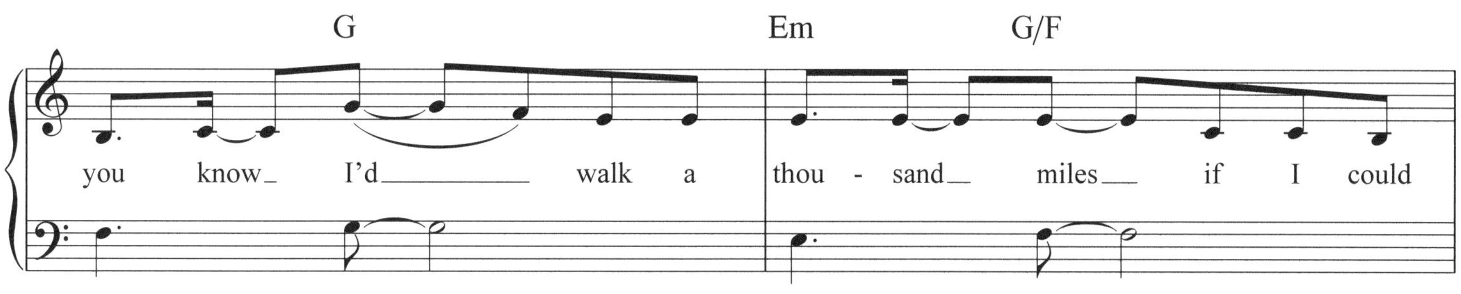
G
Em
G/F
you know I'd walk a thou - sand miles if I could

Am
G/B
G
just see you to -

F
G
C/E
F
G
C/E
F
- night.

G
C/E
F
G
C/E
F

Memory

Music by Andrew Lloyd Webber
Text by Trevor Nunn after T.S. Eliot

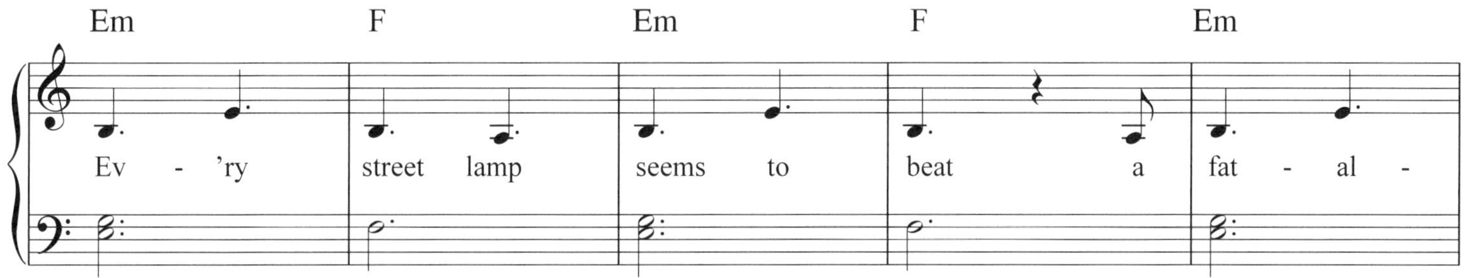
Em
F
Em
F
Em
Ev - 'ry
street lamp
seems to
beat a
fat - al -

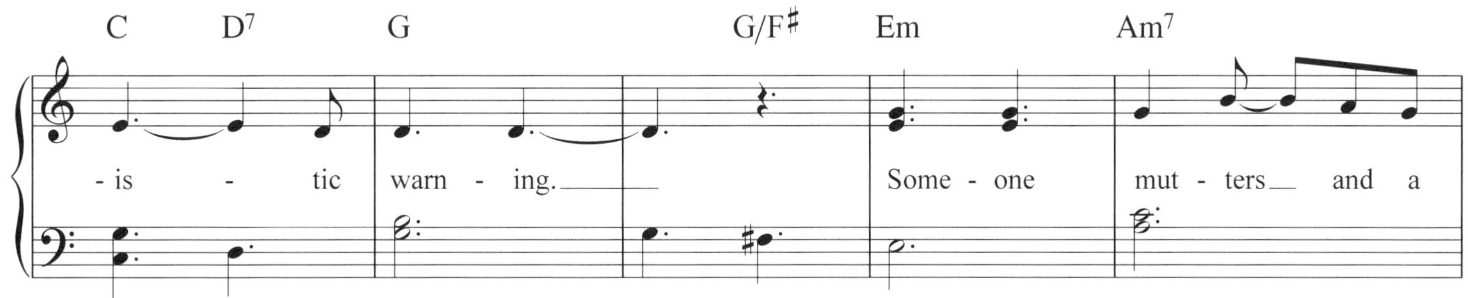
C
D7
G
G/F♯
Em
Am7
- is - tic
warn - ing.
Some - one
mut - ters and a

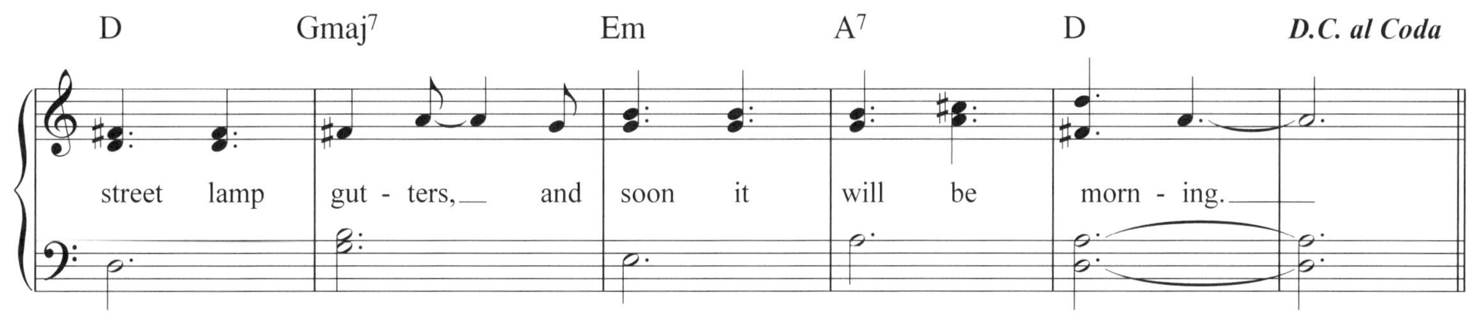
D
Gmaj7
Em
A7
D
D.C. al Coda
street lamp
gut - ters, and
soon it
will be
morn - ing.

Coda
C5
rit.

Nothing Compares 2 U

Words & Music by Prince

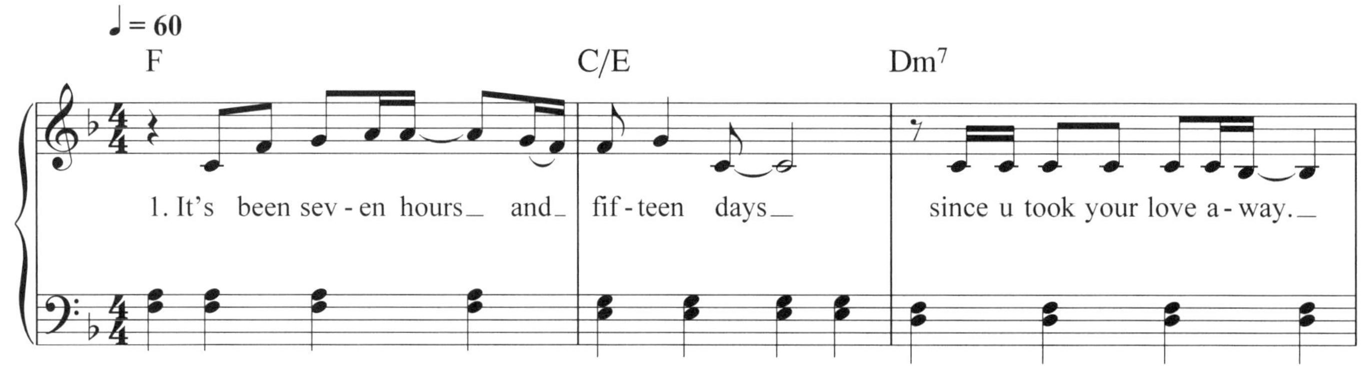

F
C7sus4
F
I can eat my din - ner at a fan - cy
C/E
res - tau - rant.
But
Dm7
noth - ing,
I said noth - ing can take a - way
A7
these blues.
'Cause
E♭
B♭
noth - ing com - pares,
E♭
B♭
noth - ing com - pares 2 u.
C
F
2. It's been so lone - ly with -
3. (Instrumental)
C/E
out u here,
3
Dm7
like a bird with - out a song.
F
Csus4
Ah.
F
Noth - ing can stop these lone - ly

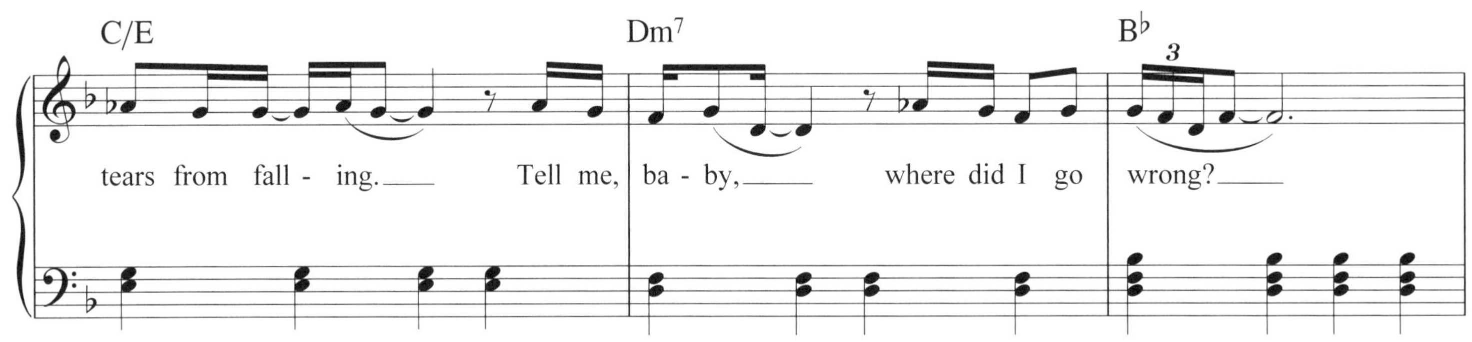
C/E
Dm7
B♭
3
tears from fall - ing. Tell me, ba - by, where did I go wrong?

F
C/E
3
(freely) I could put my arms a - round ev - 'ry boy I see,
All the flow - ers that u plant - ed, Ma - ma, in the back yard

Dm7
F
Csus4
but they'd on - ly re - mind me of u.
all died when u went a - way.
Ah.

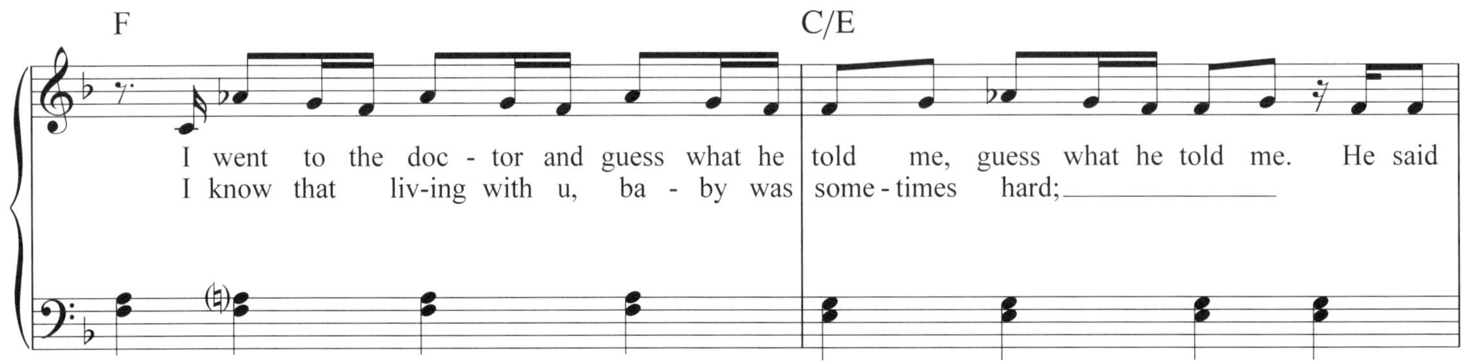
F
C/E
I went to the doc - tor and guess what he told me, guess what he told me. He said
I know that liv-ing with u, ba - by was some - times hard;

A7
"Girl, u bet - ter try 2 have fun, don't mat - ter what u do. But he's a fool; 'cause
but I'm will - ing 2 give it an - oth - er try.
E♭ B♭ Dm C
1.
noth - ing com - pares, noth-ing com-pares 2 u.
noth - ing com - pares, noth-ing com-pares 2 u.
2.
E♭ B♭ Dm C
Noth - ing com - pares, noth - ing com - pares 2 u.
E♭ B♭ Dm C
Noth-ing com - pares, noth - ing com-pares 2 u.
E♭ B♭ Dm C
Repeat to fade

Patience

Words & Music by Mark Owen, Gary Barlow, Jason Orange,
Howard Donald & John Shanks

Moderate ballad ♩ = 90

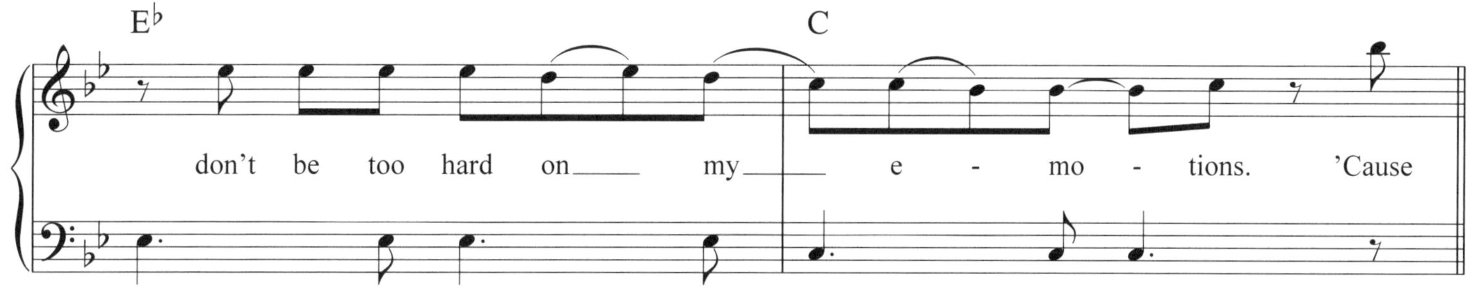
E♭
C
don't be too hard on my e - mo - tions. 'Cause

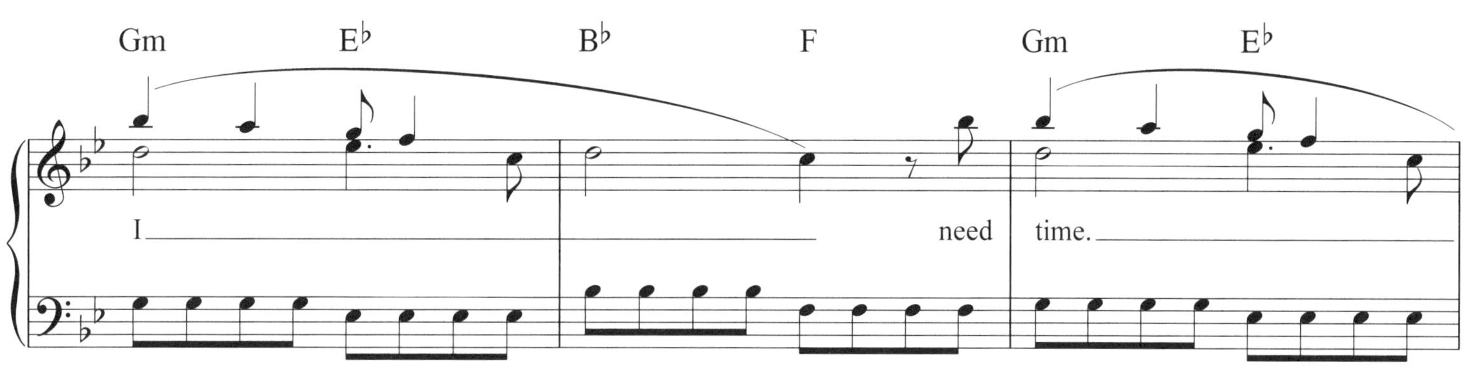
Gm
E♭
B♭
F
Gm
E♭
I need time.

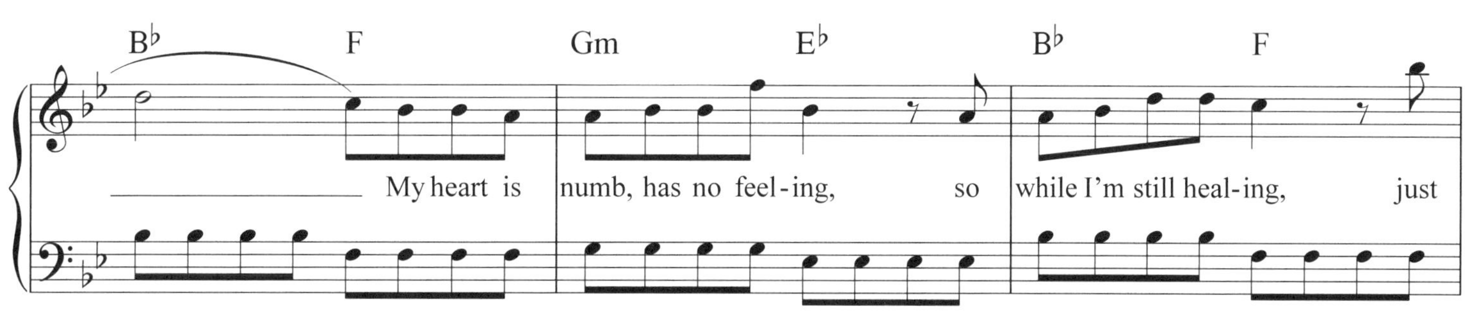
B♭
F
Gm
E♭
B♭
F
My heart is numb, has no feel-ing, so while I'm still heal-ing, just

Gm
E♭
B♭
F
Gm
try and have a lit-tle pa - tience.

Red, Red Wine

Words & Music by Neil Diamond

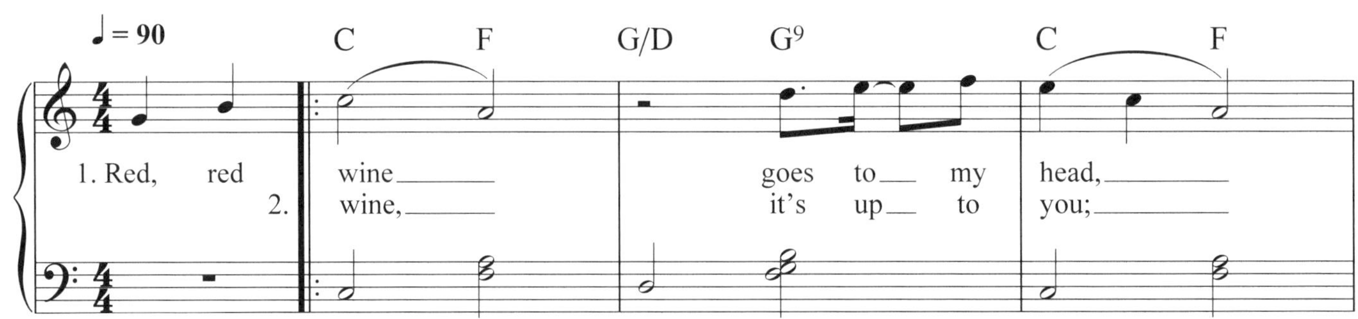

G C F G
wrong, now I've found just one thing makes me for - get. Red, red

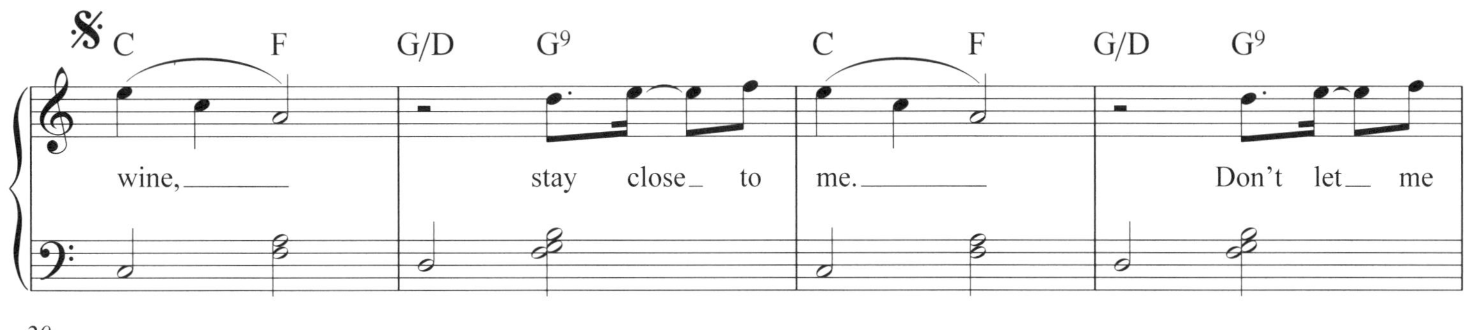
C F G/D G^9 C F G/D G^9
wine, stay close to me. Don't let me
20

1.
C F G/D G^9 G F G^7
be a - lone it's tear - ing a - part my blue, blue heart.

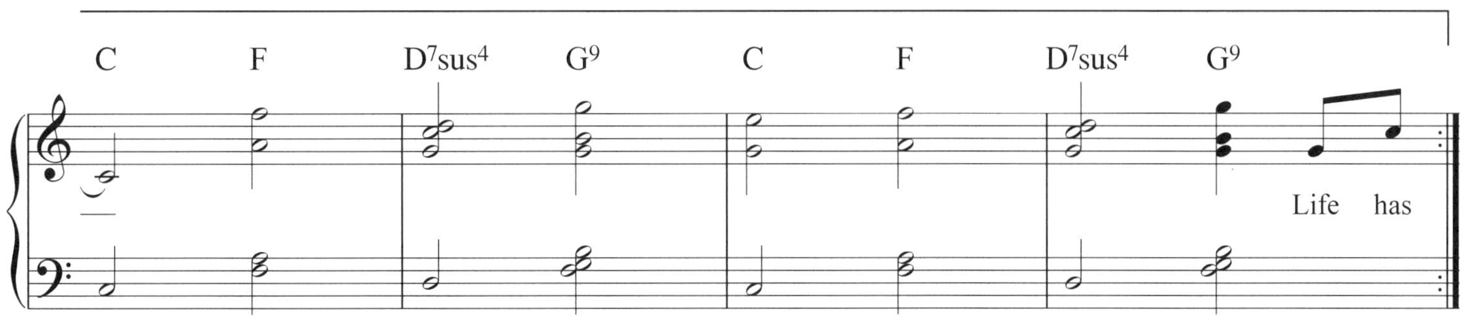
C F D^{7}sus^4 G^9 C F D^{7}sus^4 G^9
Life has

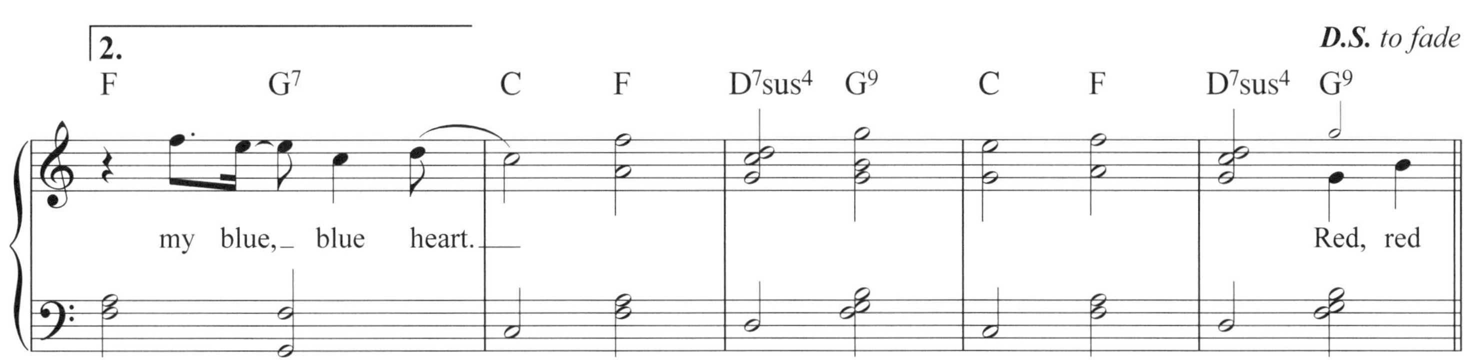
2.
D.S. to fade
F G^7 C F D^{7}sus^4 G^9 C F D^{7}sus^4 G^9
my blue, blue heart. Red, red

Run

Words & Music by Gary Lightbody, Jonathan Quinn,
Mark McClelland, Nathan Connolly & Iain Archer

With a slow beat ♩ = 72

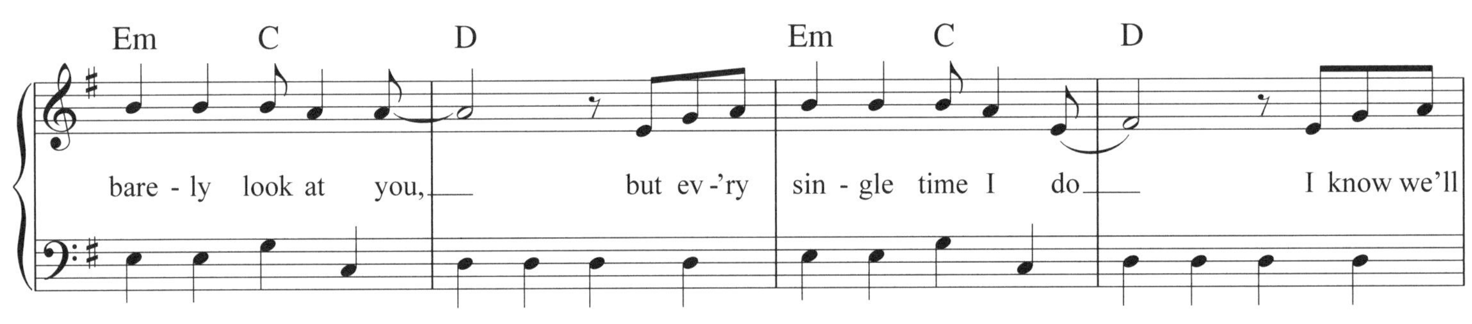

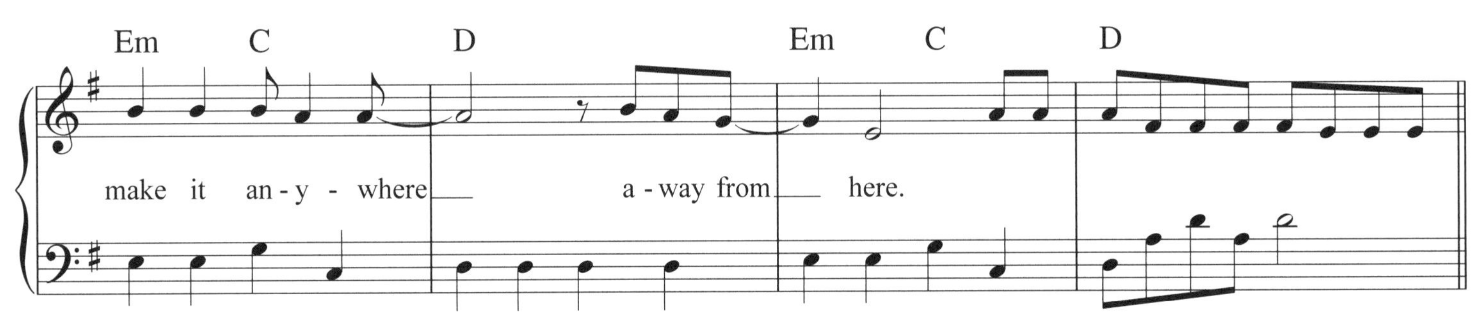

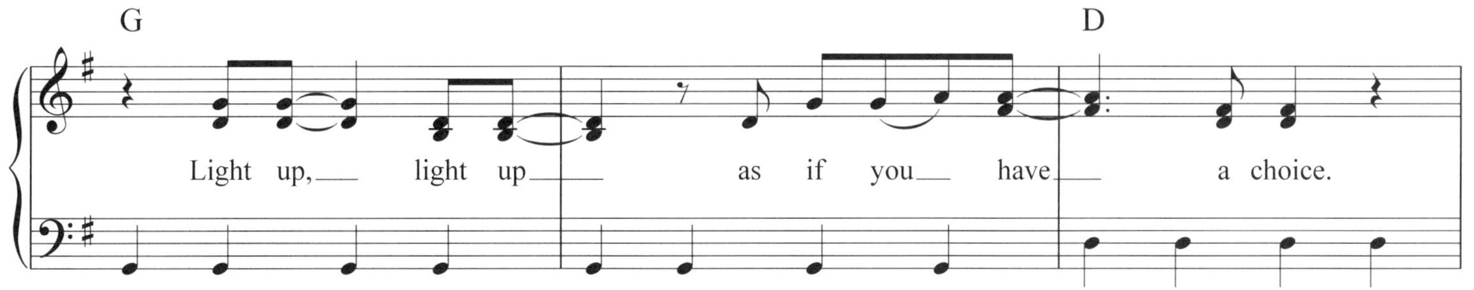
G
D
Light up, light up as if you have a choice.

Em
E - ven if you can - not hear my voice, I'll be right be - side you, dear.

C
G
Loud-er, loud-er and we'll run for

D
Em
our lives. I can hard - ly speak, I un - der - stand why

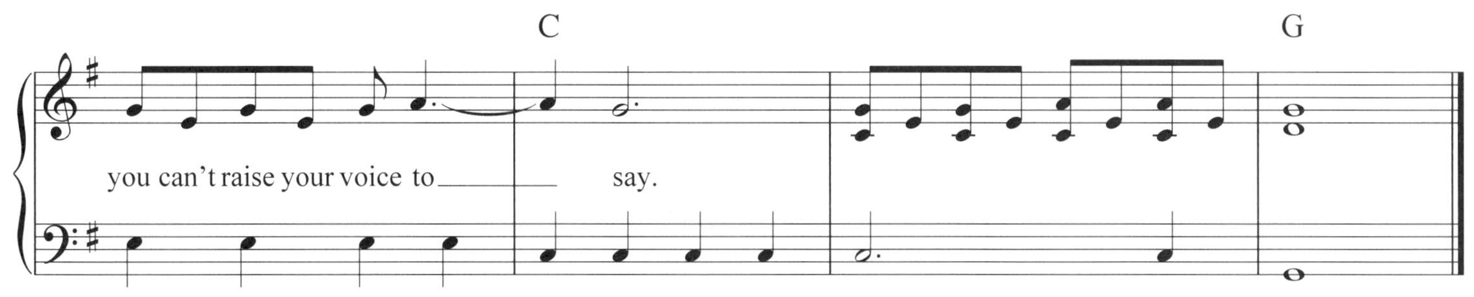
C
G
you can't raise your voice to say.

She's The One

Words & Music by Karl Wallinger

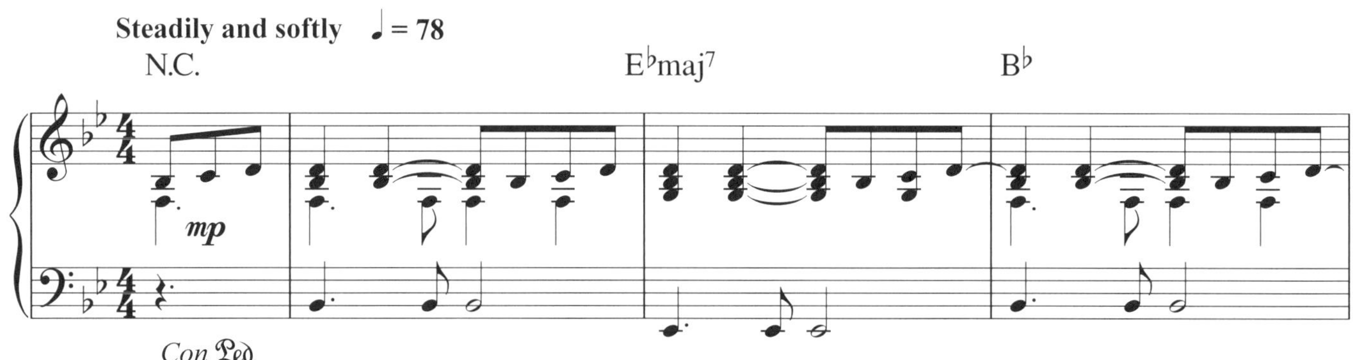

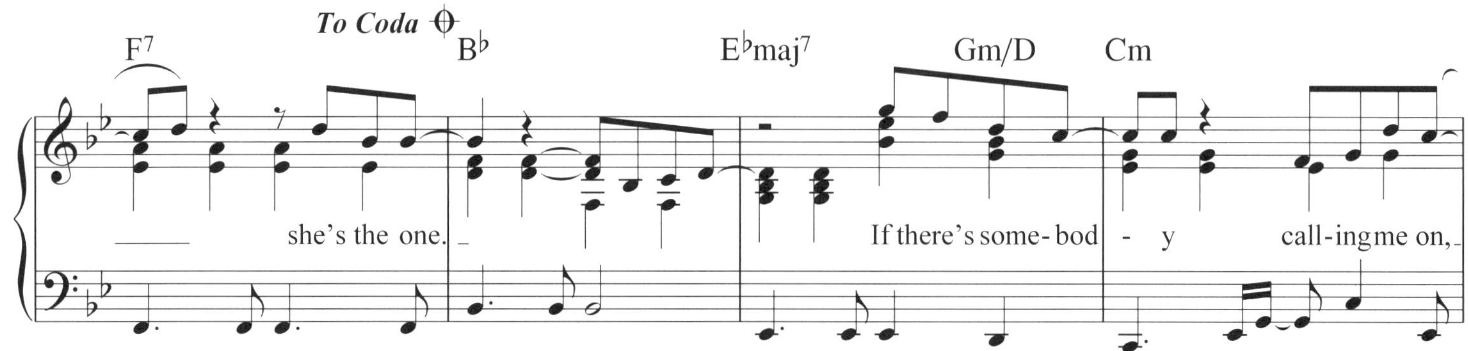

1° only
F7
B♭
E♭maj7
B♭
she's the one.
2. We were young,
we were wrong,
E♭maj7
B♭
E♭maj7
we were fine
all a - long.
If there's some -bod-
Cm
F7
B♭
B♭11
B♭7
- y.
call-ing me on,
she's the one.
E♭
When you get to where you wan-na go, and you
know the things you wan-na know, you're
B♭
B♭11
B♭7
E♭
smil - - ing.
When you said what you wan-na say and you

Cm
know the way you wan - na play, yeah.
(2.) say
You'll be so high you'll be
F11
1.
F
2.
F
D.S. al Coda
fly - - - ing.
3. Though the sea
- ing.
4. I was her,
Coda
B♭
B♭9
Cm7
If there's some - bod - y call - ing me on,
F7
B♭
B♭9
she's the one.
If there's some - bod-
Cm7
F7
Gm
- y call - ing me on,
she's the one,
yes, she's the one.

Verse 3:
Though the sea will be strong,
I know we'll carry on.
'Cause if there's somebody calling me on, she's the one.
If there's somebody calling me on, she's the one.

Verse 4:
I was her, she was me,
We were one, we were free.
And if there's somebody calling me on, she's the one.
If there's somebody calling me on, she's the one...*etc.*

Some Might Say

Words & Music by Noel Gallagher

Moderate rock ♩ = 112

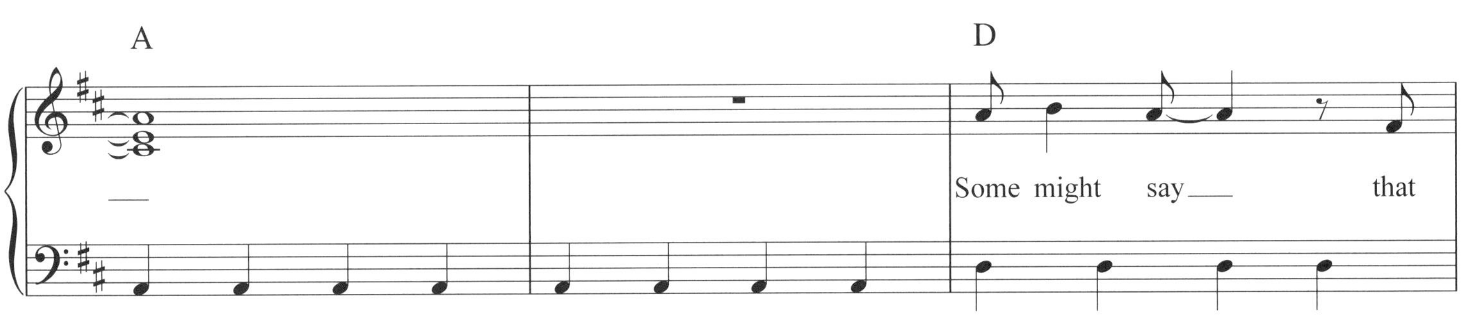

G D A
to-day 'cause they hold sway o-ver time.
Some might say,

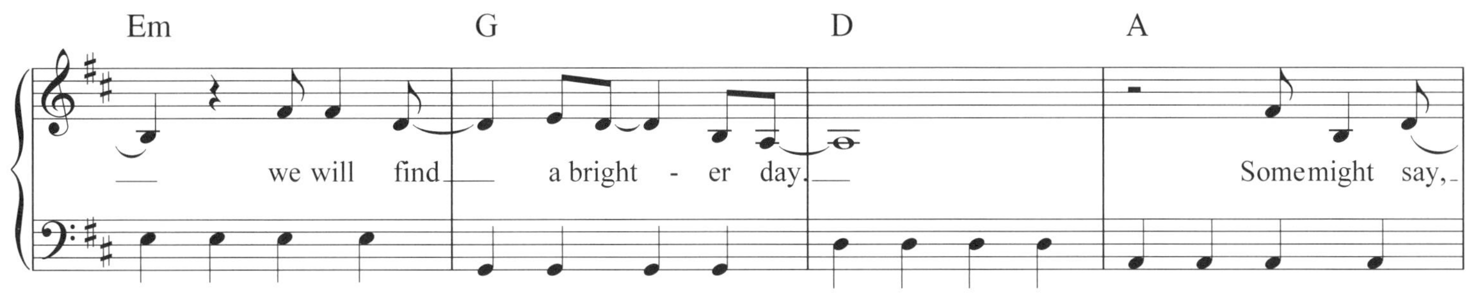
Em G D A
we will find a bright-er day.
Some might say,

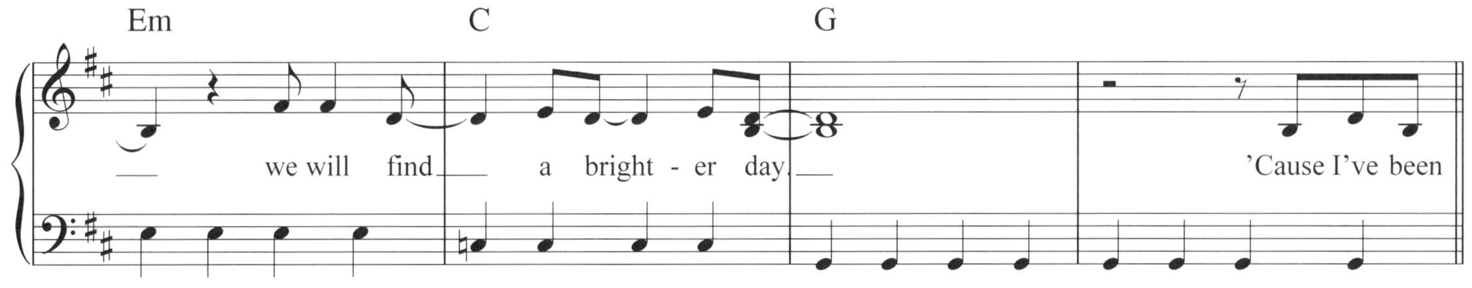
Em C G
we will find a bright-er day.
'Cause I've been

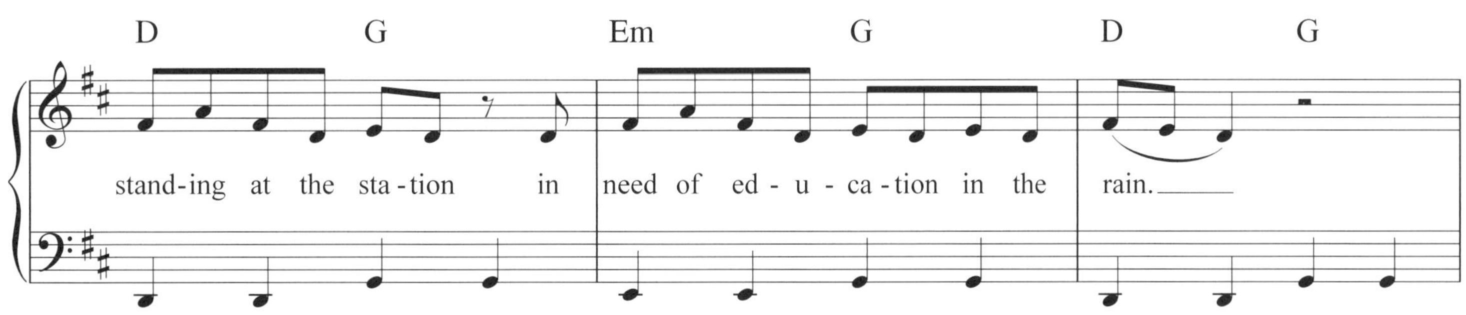
D G Em G D G
stand-ing at the sta-tion in need of ed-u-ca-tion in the rain.

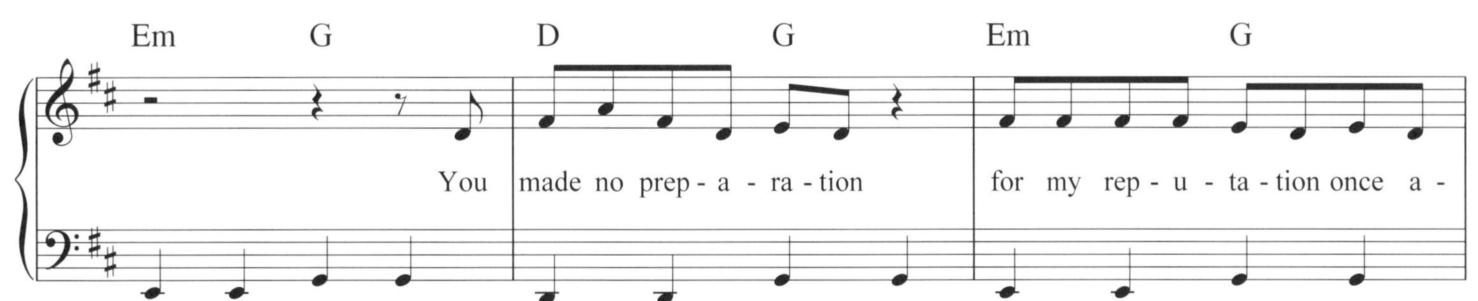
Em G D G Em G
You made no prep-a-ra-tion for my rep-u-ta-tion once a-

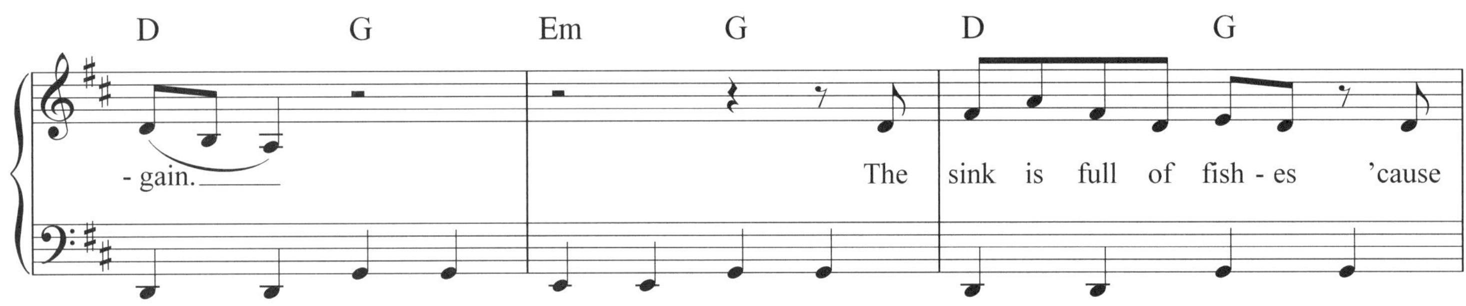
D G Em G D G
-gain. The sink is full of fish-es 'cause
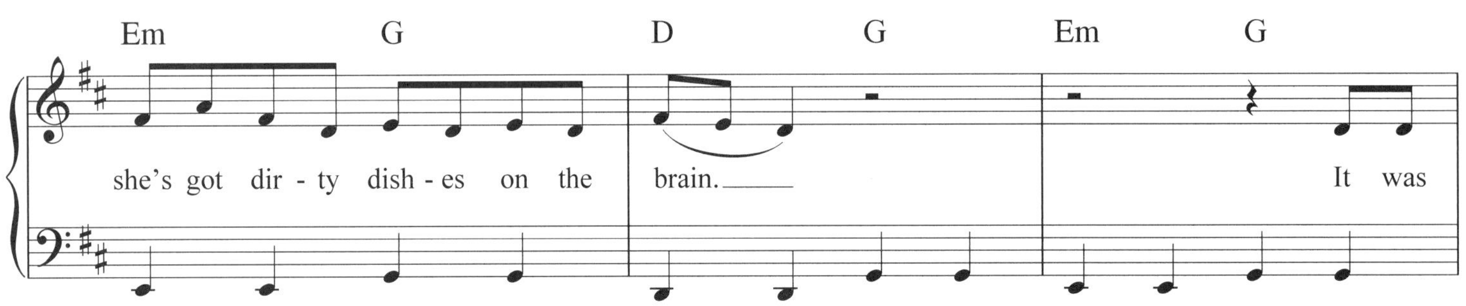
Em G D G Em G
she's got dir-ty dish-es on the brain. It was
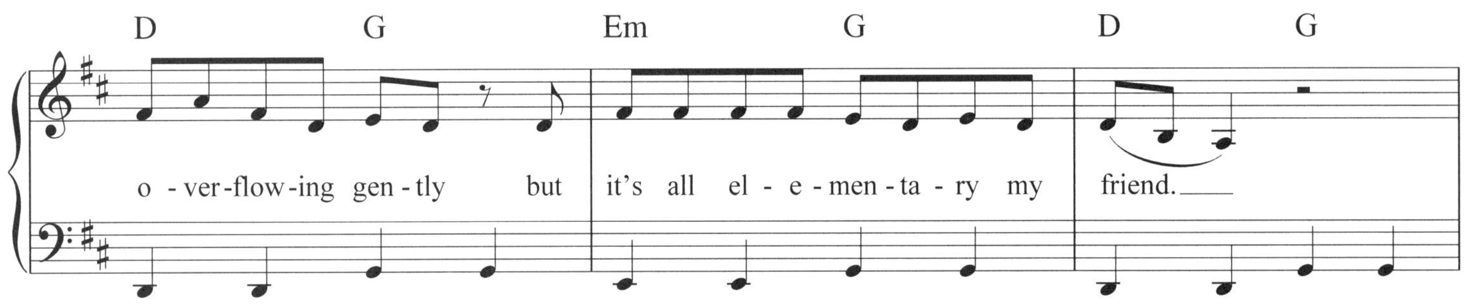
D G Em G D G
o-ver-flow-ing gen-tly but it's all el-e-men-ta-ry my friend.
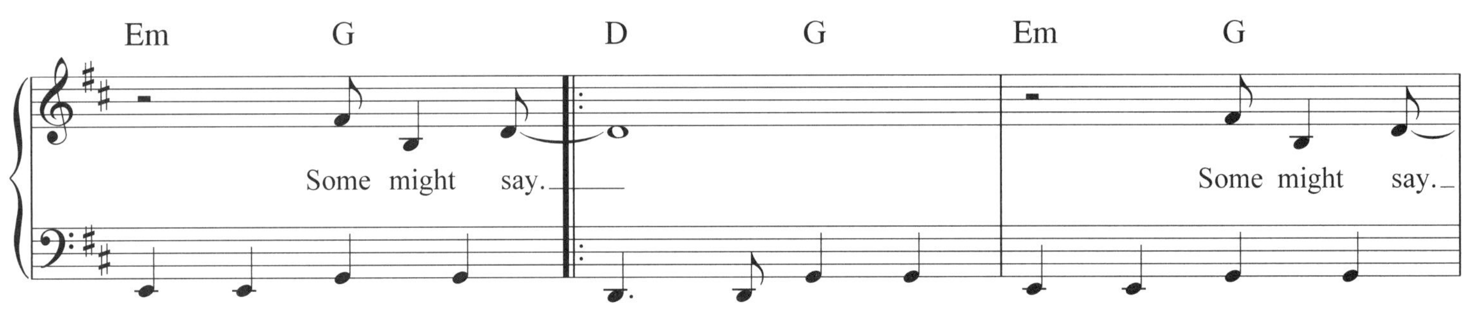
Em G D G Em G
Some might say. Some might say.
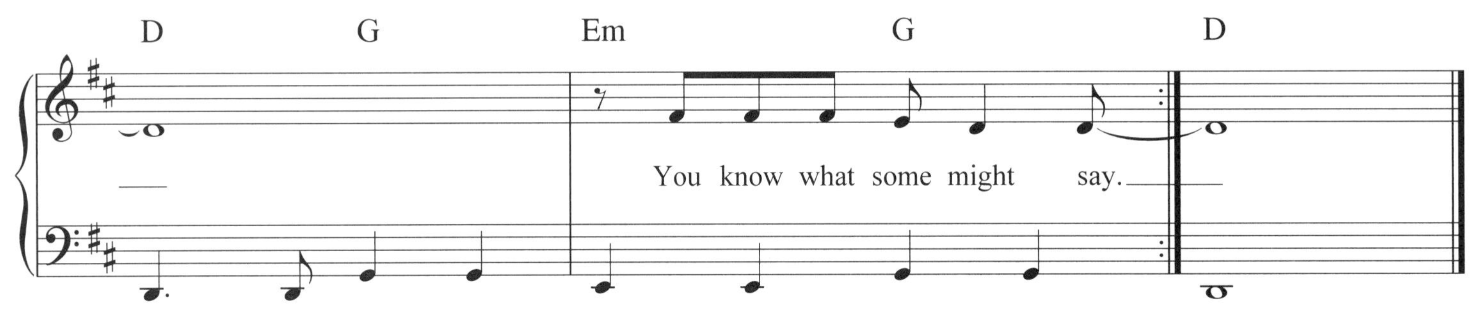
D G Em G D
You know what some might say.

Somethin' Stupid

Words & Music by C. Carson Parks

G
Dm7
G7
C
C6
af - ter-wards we drop in - to a
qui - et lit - tle place and have a
drink or two.
time is right, your per-fume fills my
head, the stars get red and oh, the
night's so blue.

E♭
Am7
D7
Am7
D7
And
then I go and spoil it all by
say - ing some - thin' stu - pid like I

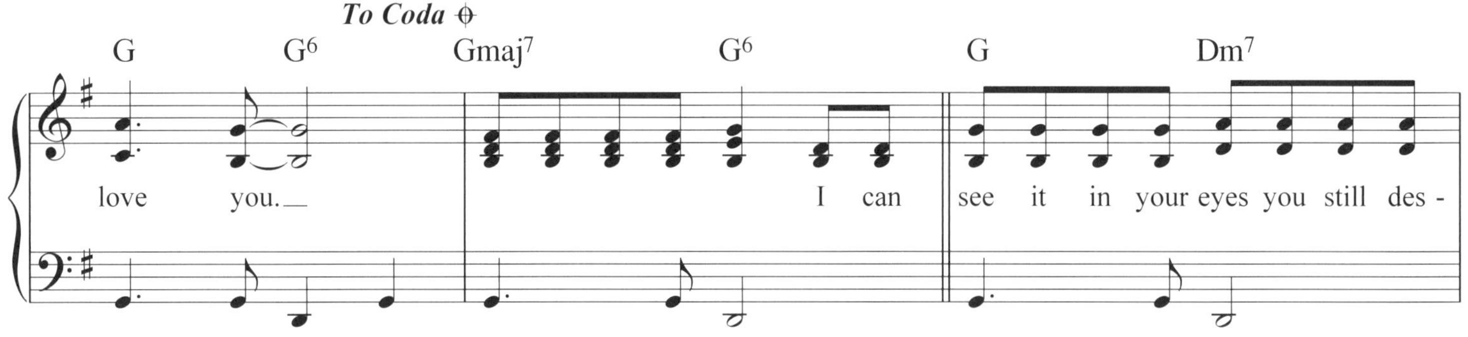
To Coda
G
G6
Gmaj7
G6
G
Dm7
love you.
I can
see it in your eyes you still des -

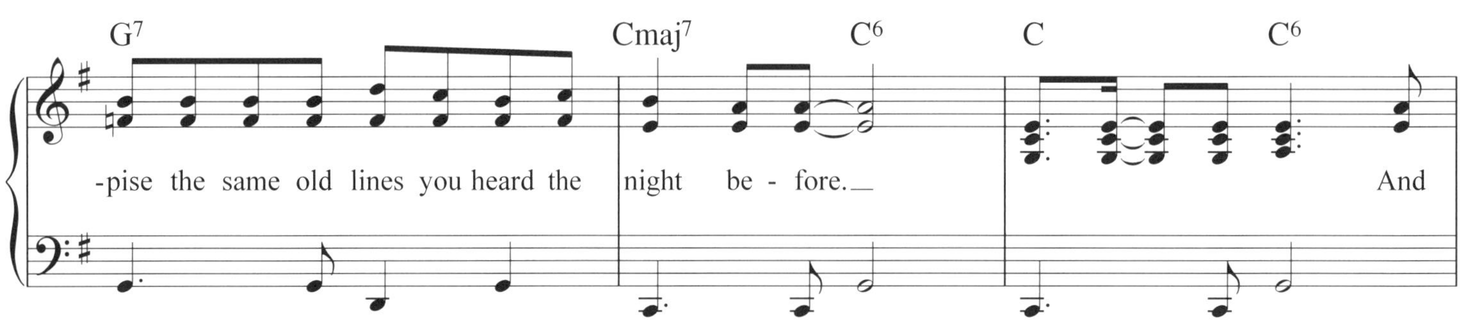
G7
Cmaj7
C6
C
C6
-pise the same old lines you heard the
night be - fore.
And

D.S. al Coda
A7
Em7
A7
D7
Daug
though it's just a line to you for
me it's true and nev - er seemed so
right be-fore.

Coda
Gmaj7
G6
G
G6
Gmaj7
G6
Am7
D7
Am7
D7
Am7
D7
Am7
D7
G
G6
Gmaj7
G6
The
G7
Dm7
G7
Cmaj7
C6
time is right, your per-fume fills my
head, the skies get red and oh, the
night's so blue,
E♭
Am7
D7
Am7
D7
And
then I go and spoil it all by
say-ing some-thin' stu-pid like I
G
E♭
G
E♭
Repeat to fade
love you.
I
love you.
I

Sunny Afternoon

Words & Music by Ray Davies

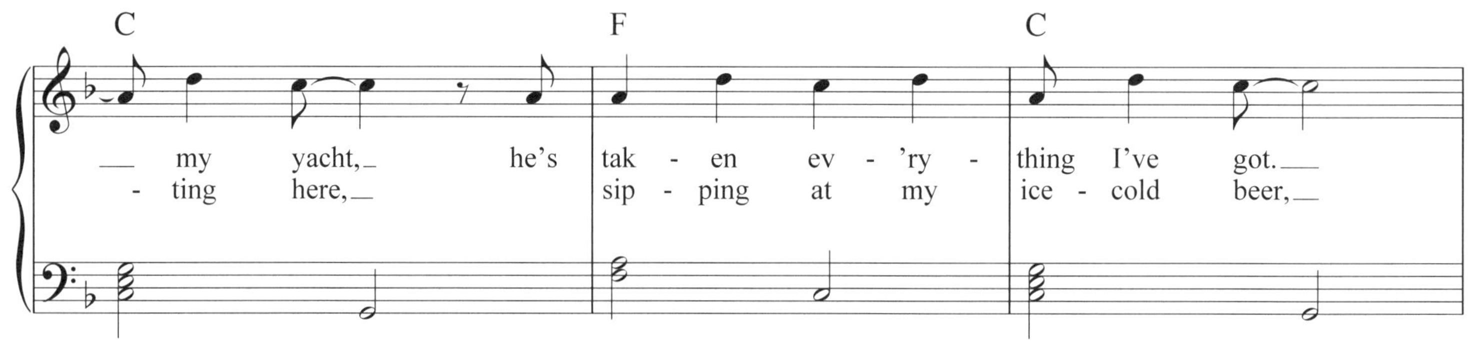

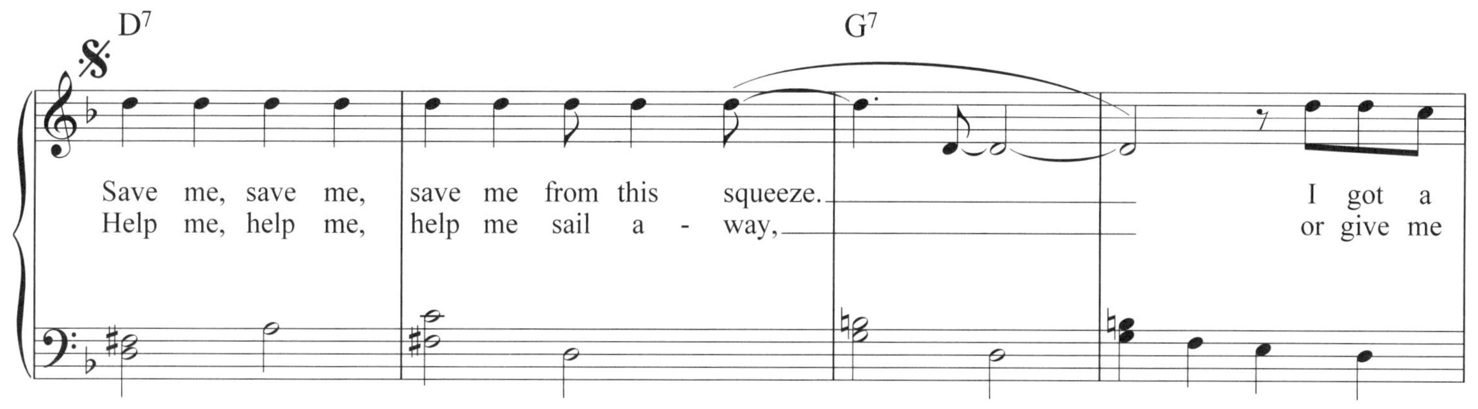
D7
G7
Save me, save me, save me from this squeeze. I got a
Help me, help me, help me sail a - way, or give me

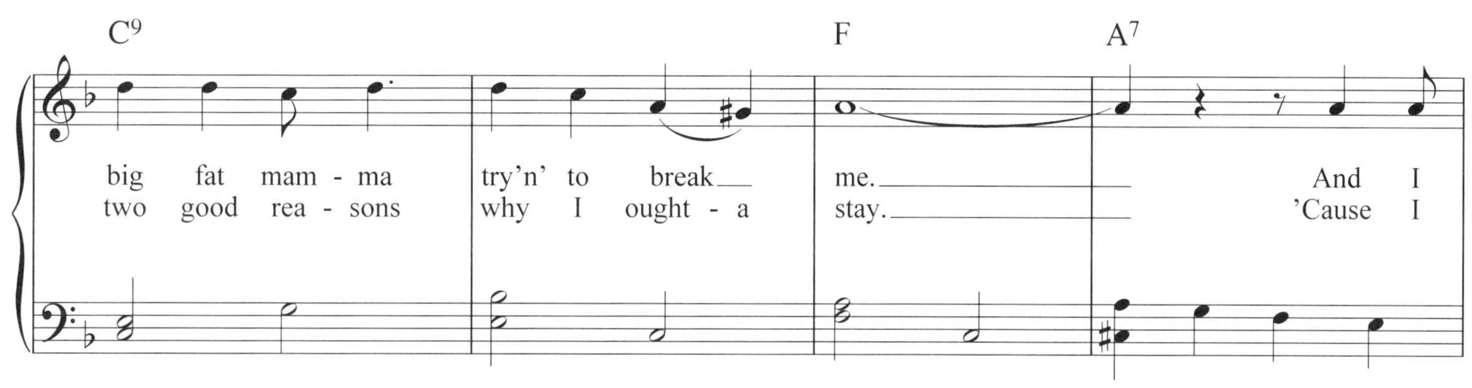
C9
F
A7
big fat mam - ma try'n' to break me. And I
two good rea - sons why I ought - a stay. 'Cause I

Dm
G7
Dm
G7
C7
love to live so pleas - ant - ly, live this life of lux - ur - y,
love to live so pleas - ant - ly, live this life of lux - ur - y,

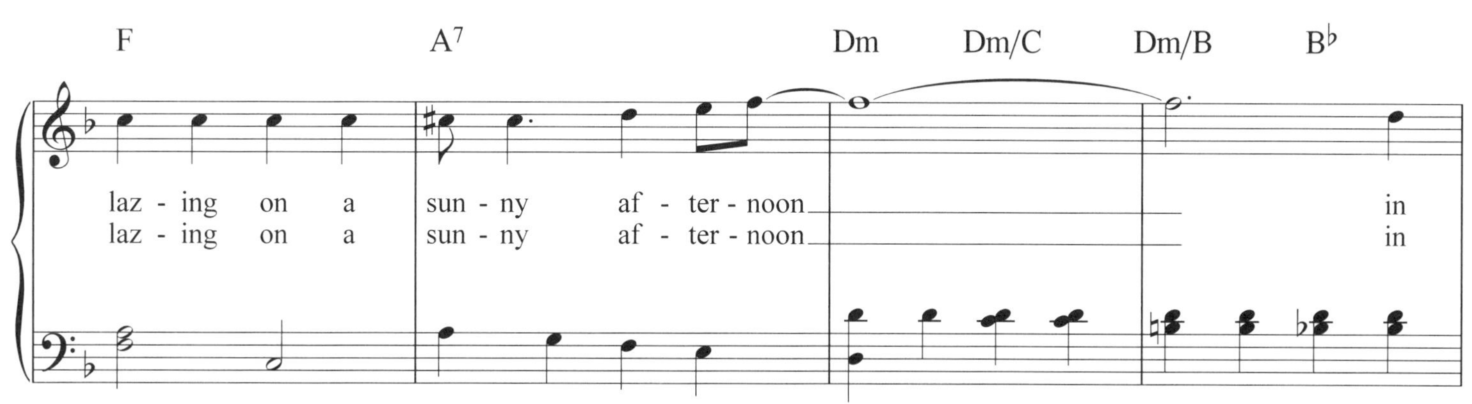
F
A7
Dm
Dm/C
Dm/B
B♭
laz - ing on a sun - ny af - ter - noon in
laz - ing on a sun - ny af - ter - noon in

To Coda
Dm/A Dm/G A7/F A7/E Dm Dm/C Dm/B B♭
sum - mer - time, in sum - mer - time, in
sum - mer - time, in sum - mer - time, in

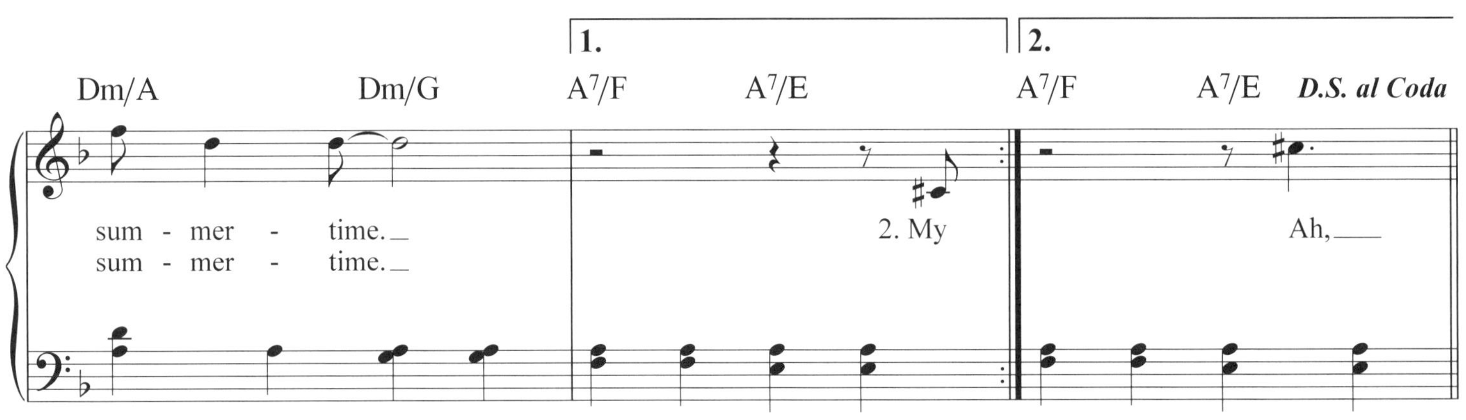
1. 2.
Dm/A Dm/G A7/F A7/E A7/F A7/E D.S. al Coda
sum - mer - time. 2. My Ah,
sum - mer - time.

Coda
Dm/A Dm/G A7/F A7/E Dm Dm/C
sum - mer - time, in sum - mer - time,

Dm/B B♭ Dm/A Dm/G A7/F A7/E Dm
in sum - mer - time.

What A Wonderful World

Words & Music by George Weiss & Bob Thiele

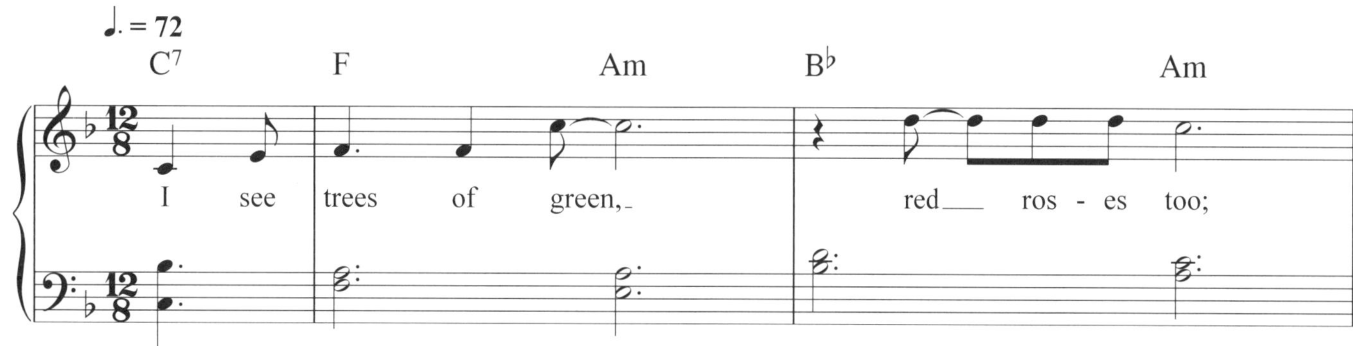

A7
Dm
D♭
the dark sa - cred night. And I think to my - self,

Gm7
C7
2
F
Gm7/F
Gm
Fmaj7
what a won - der - ful world. The

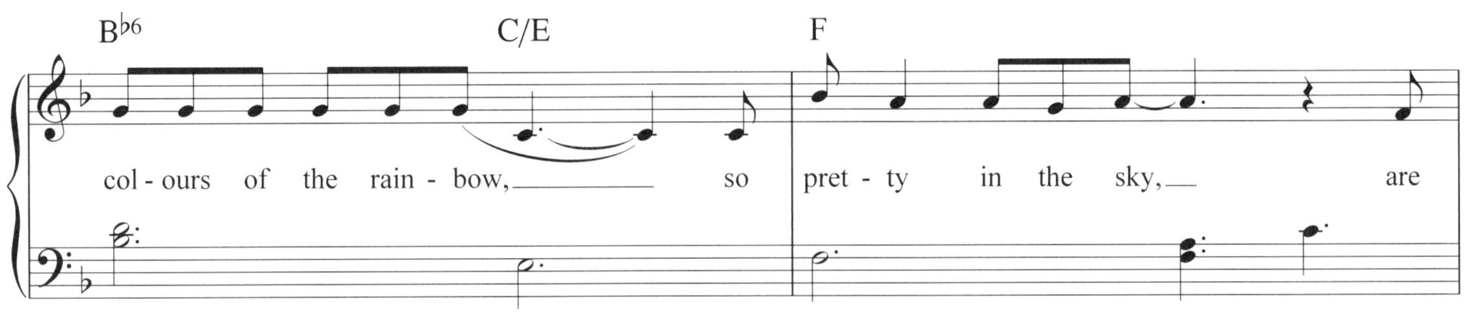
B♭6
C/E
F
col - ours of the rain - bow, so pret - ty in the sky, are

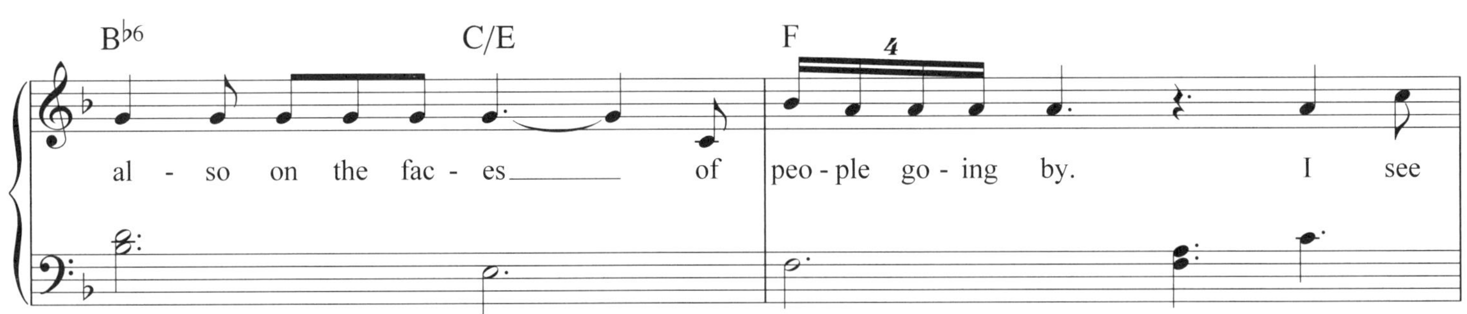
B♭6
C/E
F
4
al - so on the fac - es of peo - ple go - ing by. I see

Dm
C/E
F
C
friends shak - ing hands, say - ing "How do you do?"

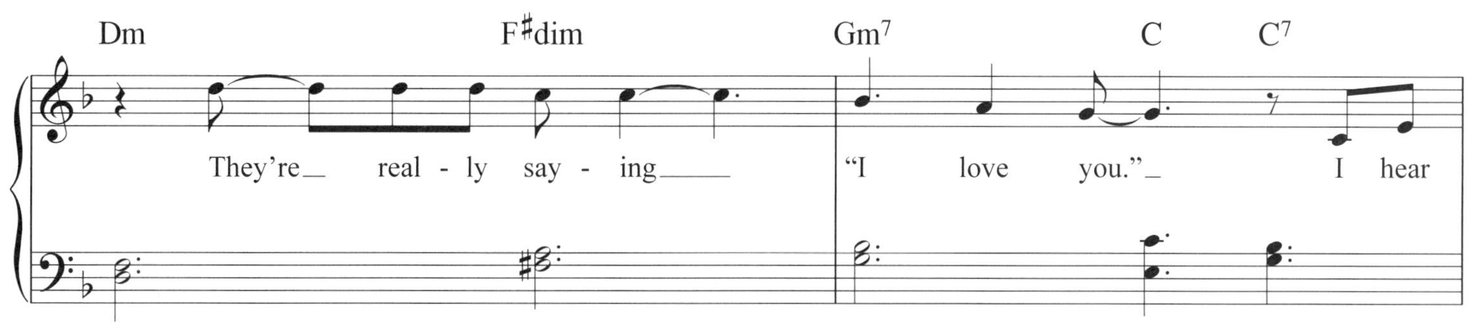
Dm
F♯dim
Gm7
C
C7
They're_ real - ly say - ing___
"I love you."_ I hear

F
Am
B♭
Am
Gm
F
ba - bies cry - ing,
I watch them grow.
They'll learn much more

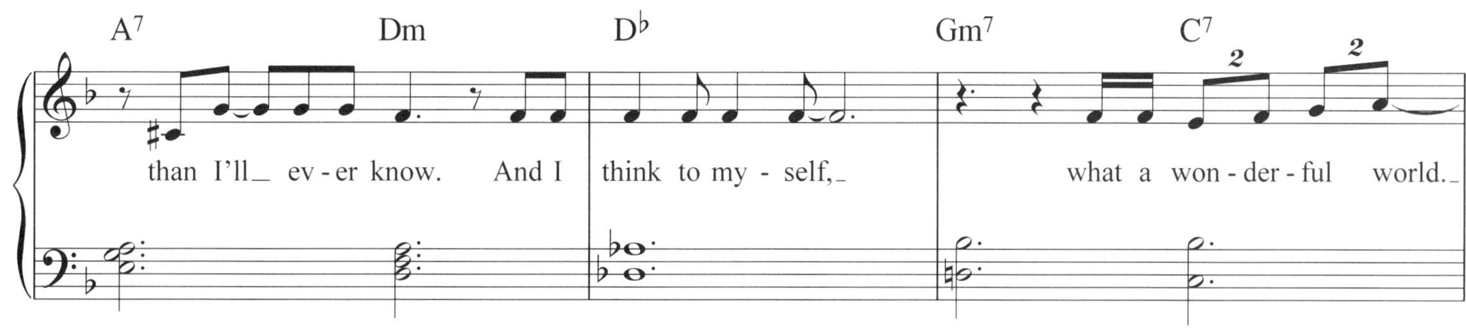
A7
Dm
D♭
Gm7
C7
than I'll_ ev - er know. And I
think to my - self,_
what a won - der - ful world._

F
E♭(♭5)
D
D7
Gm7
Yes,___ I
think to my - self,___

C7(♭9)
F
what a won - der - ful
world.
Oh, yes.

This Year's Love

Words & Music by David Gray

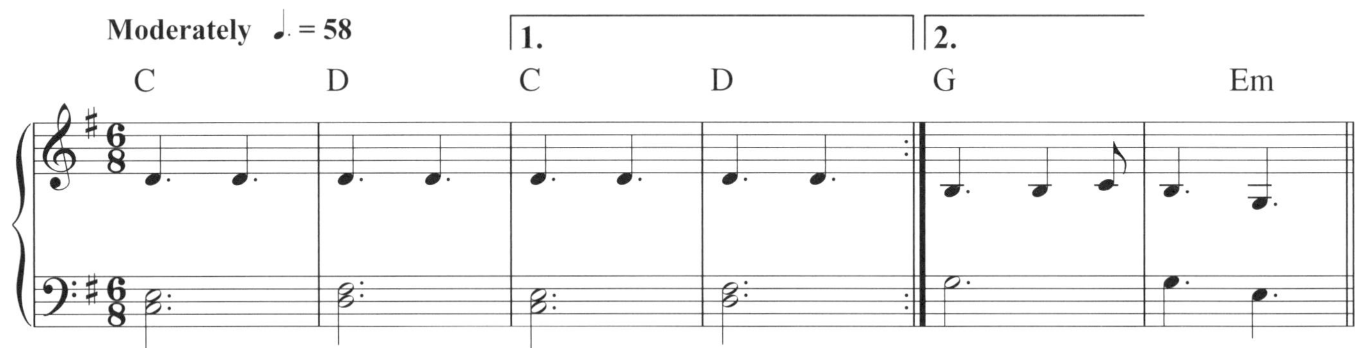

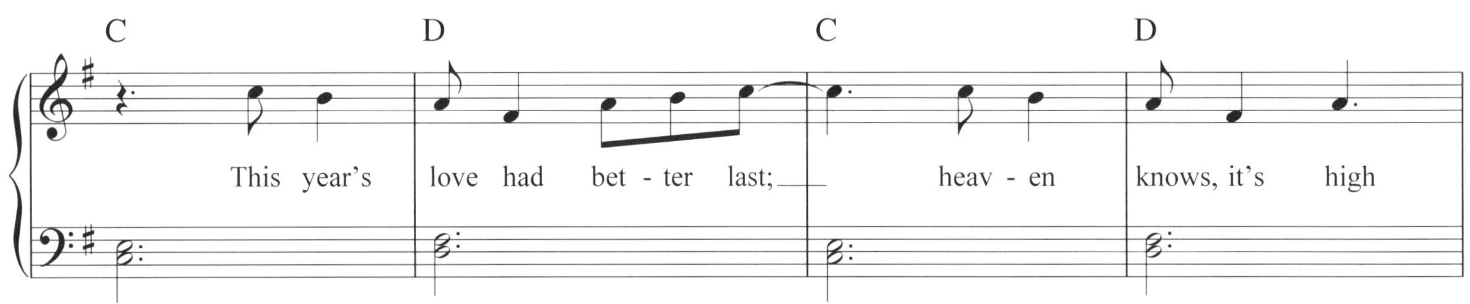

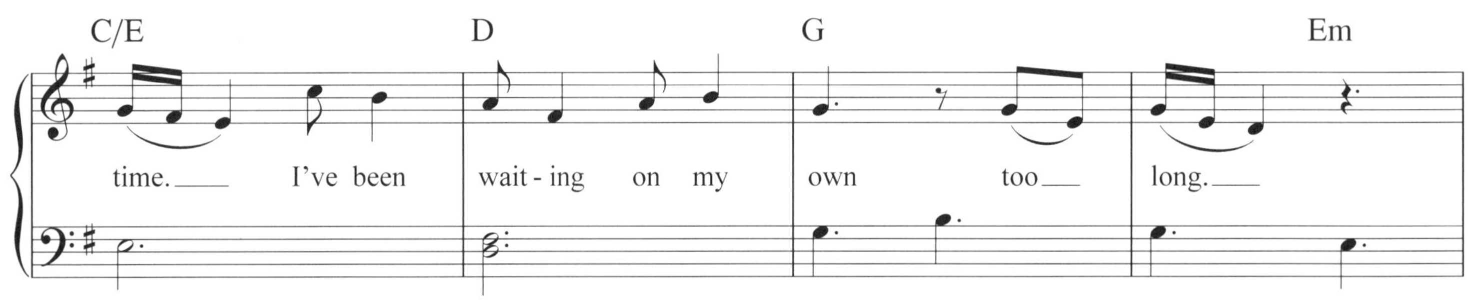

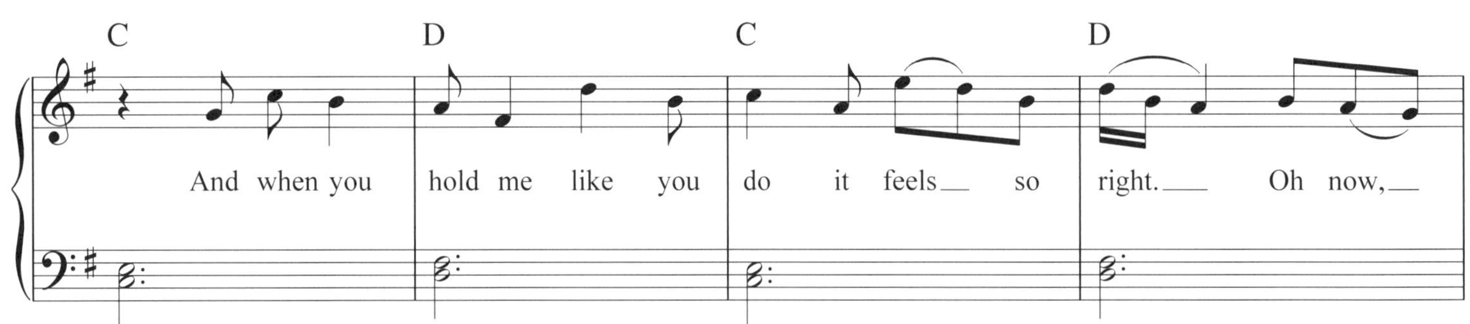

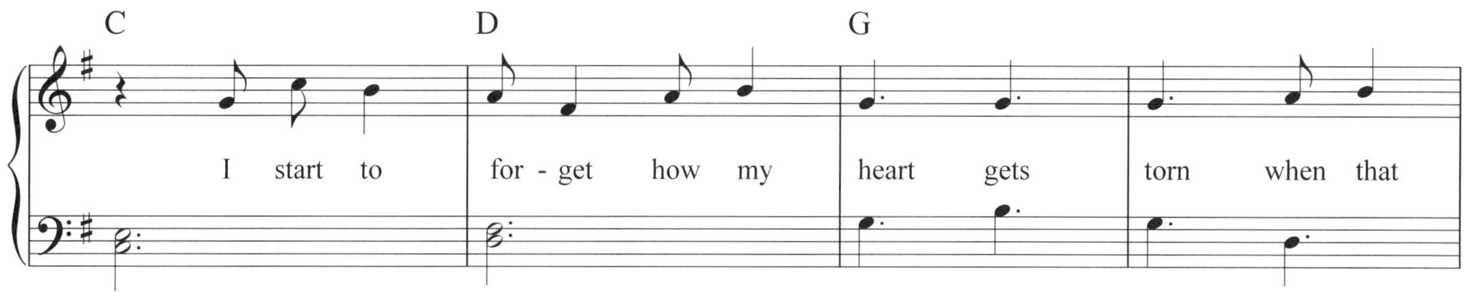
C
D
G
I start to
for - get how my
heart gets
torn when that

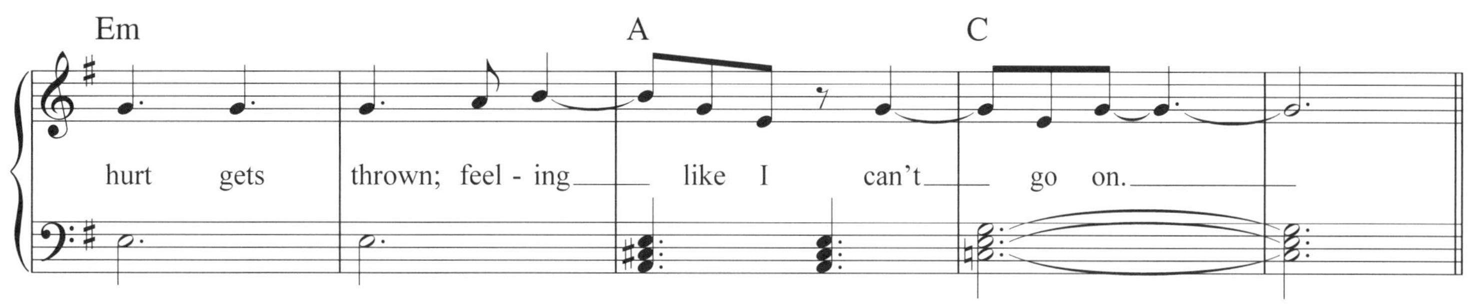
Em
A
C
hurt gets
thrown; feel - ing
like I
can't
go on.

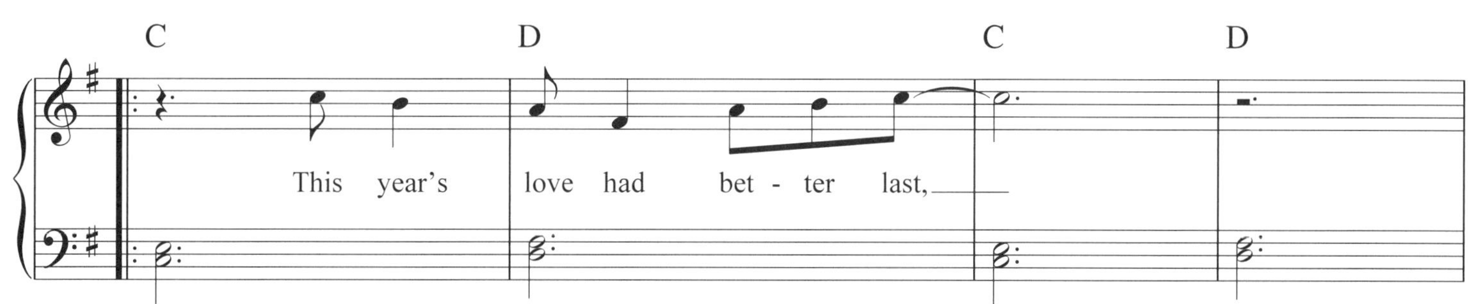
C
D
C
D
This year's
love had bet - ter last,

1.
C
D
C
D
this year's
love had bet - ter last.

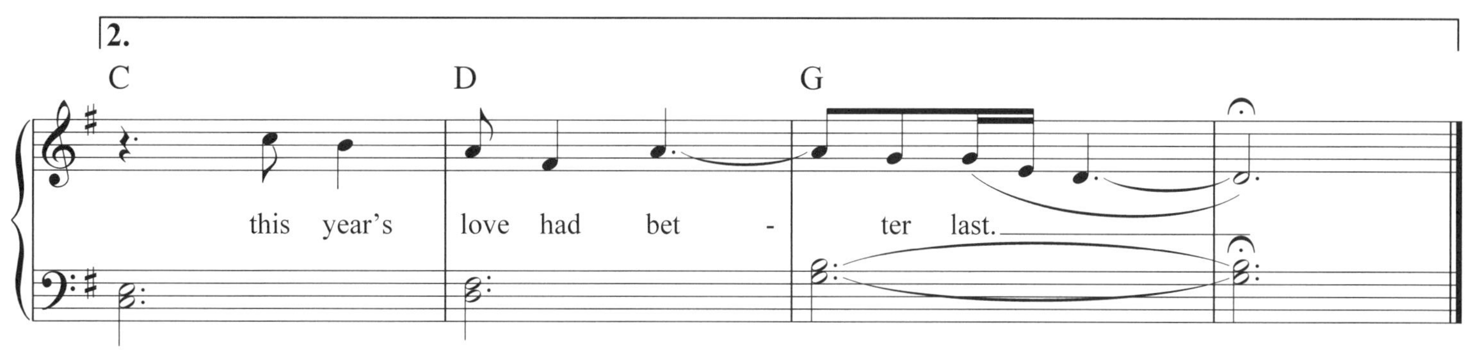
2.
C
D
G
this year's
love had bet -
ter last.

Thriller

Words & Music by Rod Temperton

With a driving beat ♩ = 118

G7
Dm7
B♭maj7
as
hor-ror looks you right be-tween the eyes;
you're par-a-lysed.

Am7
Dm F
G Dm
G7
'Cause this is
thrill-er,
thrill-er night, and
no-one's gon-na save you from the beast

Gm7
Dm F
G Dm
a-bout to strike. You know it's
thrill - er,
thrill - er night; you're

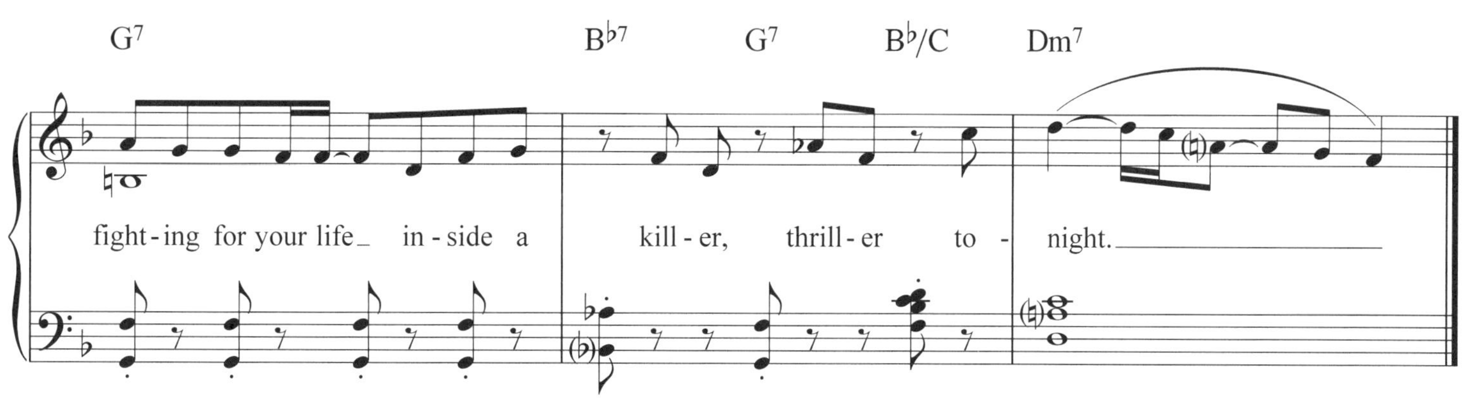
G7
B♭7
G7
B♭/C
Dm7
fight-ing for your life in-side a
kill-er, thrill-er to-
night.

The Tide Is High (Get The Feeling)

Words & Music by John Holt, Bill Padley, Howard Barrett,
Jem Godfrey & Tyrone Evans

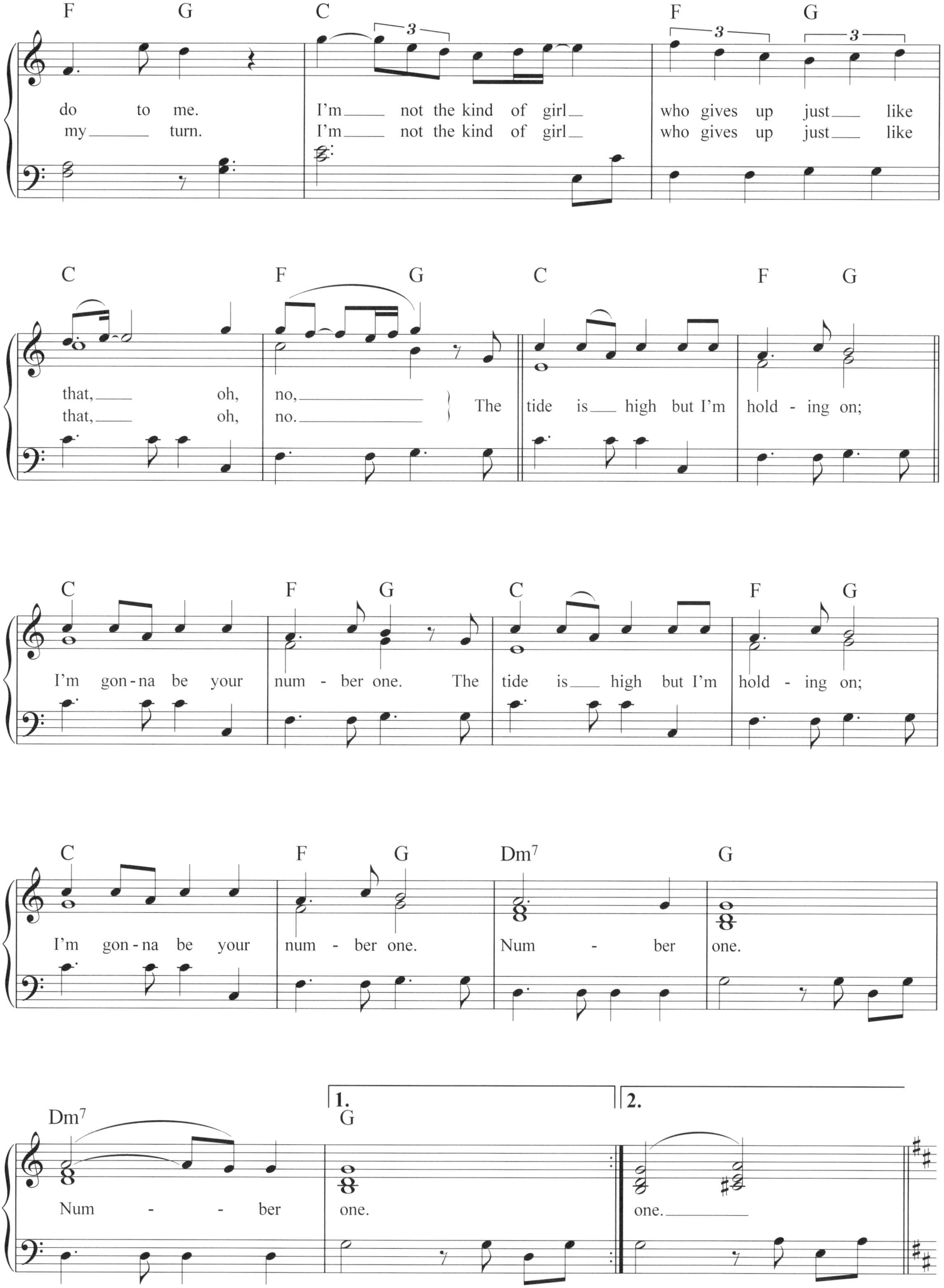

F G C F G

do to me. I'm not the kind of girl who gives up just like
my turn. I'm not the kind of girl who gives up just like

C F G C F G

that, oh, no, The tide is high but I'm hold - ing on;
that, oh, no.

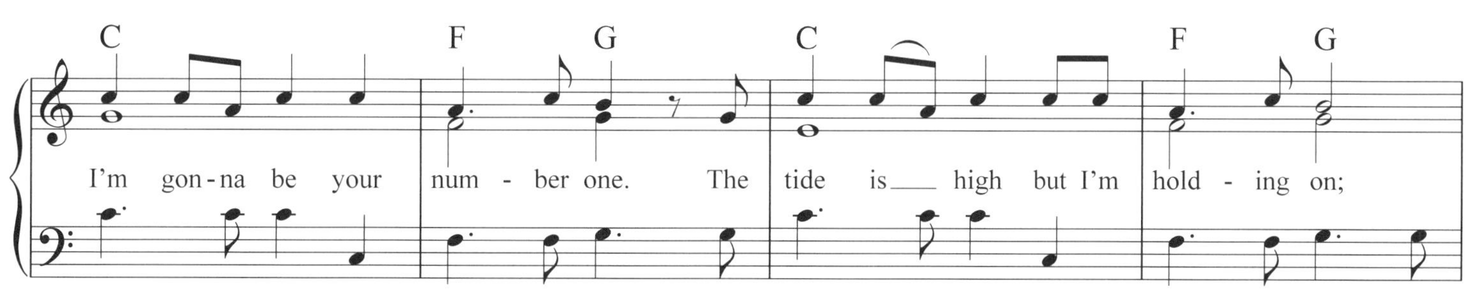

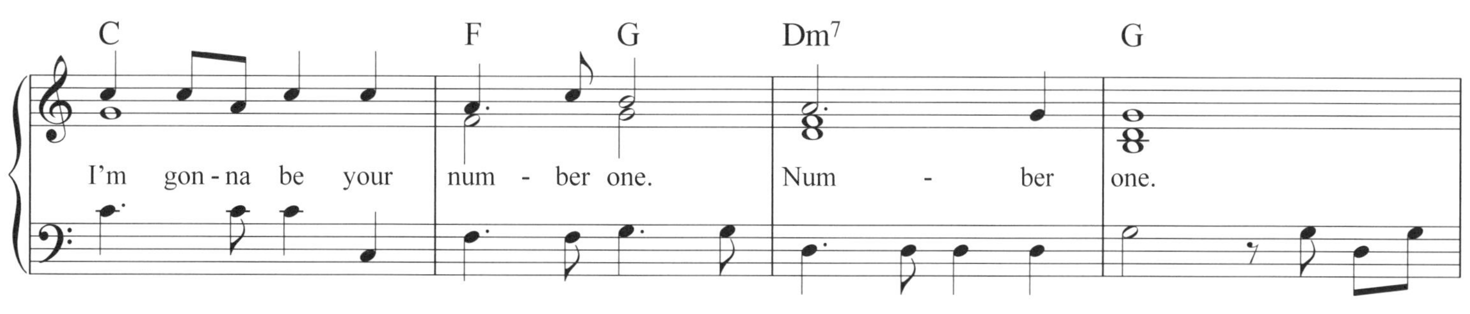

D
G
A
5. Ev - 'ry time that I get the feel - ing,
you give me some-thing to be - lieve in.

D
G
A
Ev - 'ry time that I got you near me,
I know the way that I want it to be.

D
G
A
But you know I'm gon - na take my chance now,
I'm gon - na make it hap - pen some - how.

D
G
A
And you know I can take the pres - sure; a
mo - ment's pain for a life - time's plea - sure.

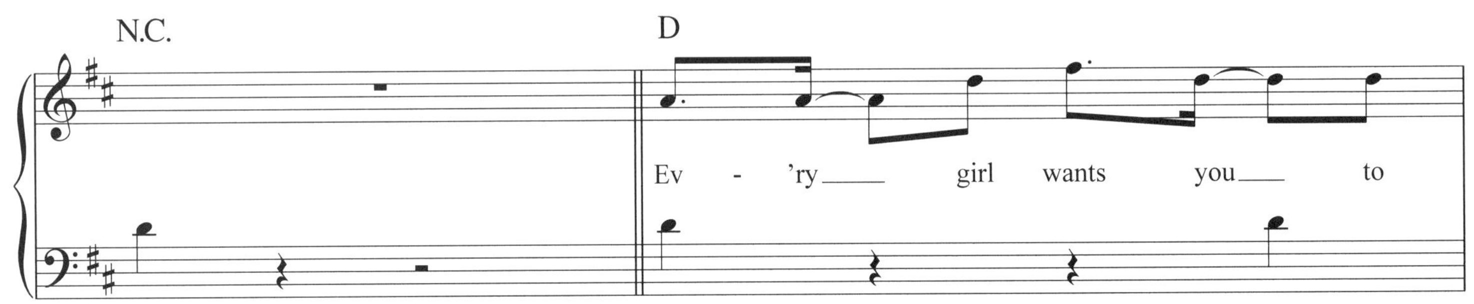
N.C.
D
Ev - 'ry girl wants you to

G A D G A
be her_ man, but I'll wait right here till_ it's my_ turn.

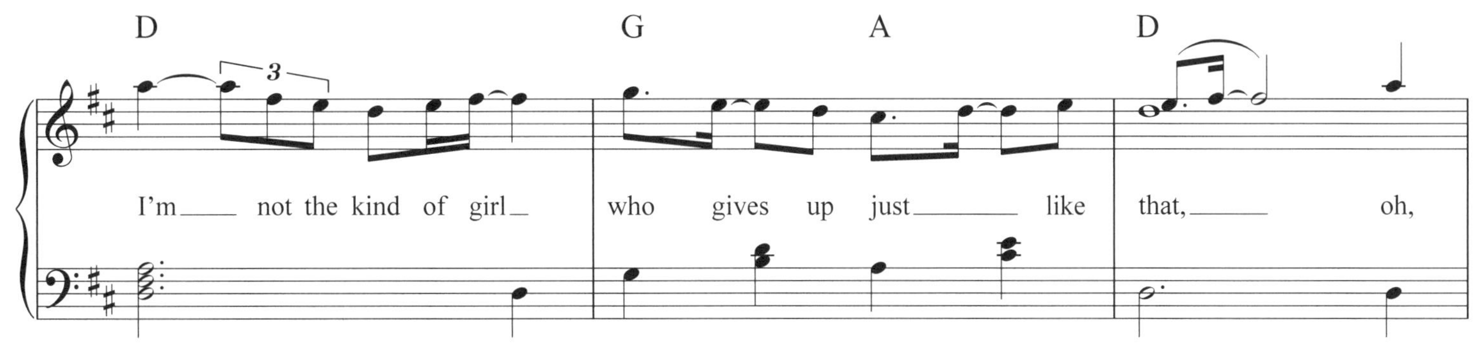
D G A D
3
I'm_ not the kind of girl_ who gives up just_ like that,_ oh,

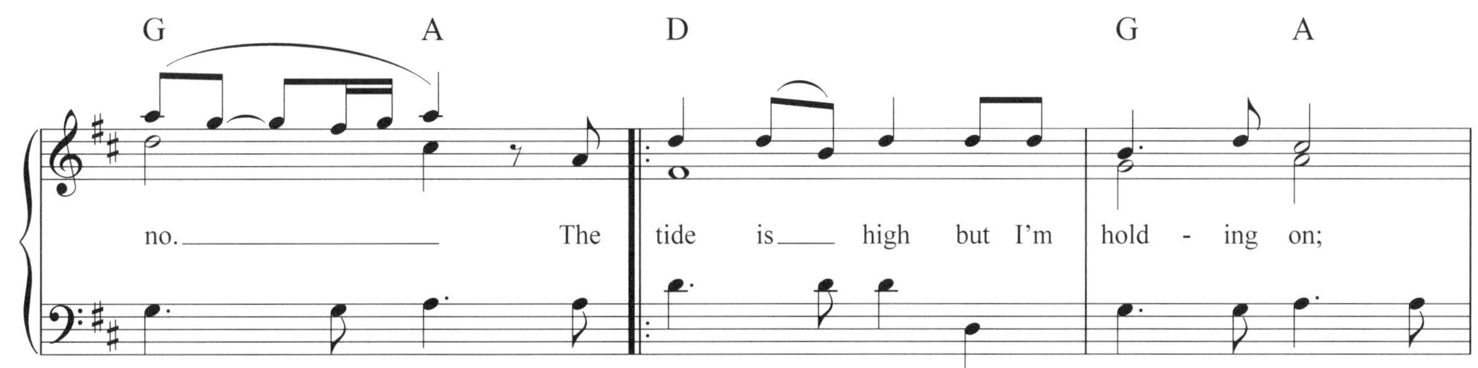
G A D G A
no._ The tide is_ high but I'm hold - ing on;

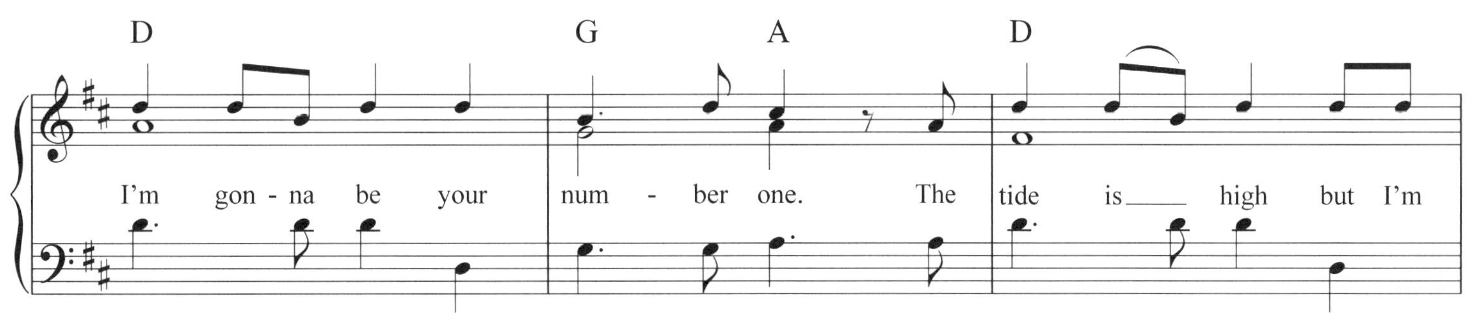
D G A D
I'm gon - na be your num - ber one. The tide is_ high but I'm

Play 3 times to fade
G A D G A
hold - ing on; I'm gon - na be your num - ber one. The

Toxic

Words & Music by Cathy Dennis, Christian Karlsson,
Pontus Winnberg & Henrik Jonback

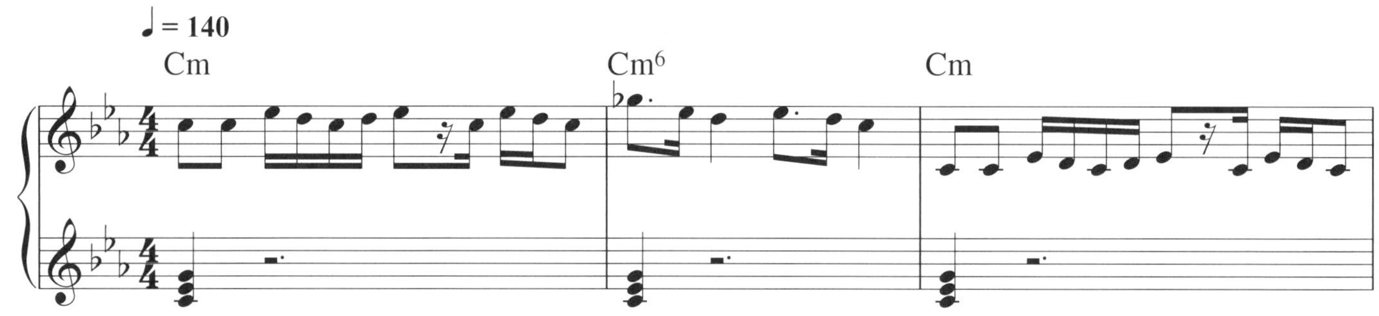

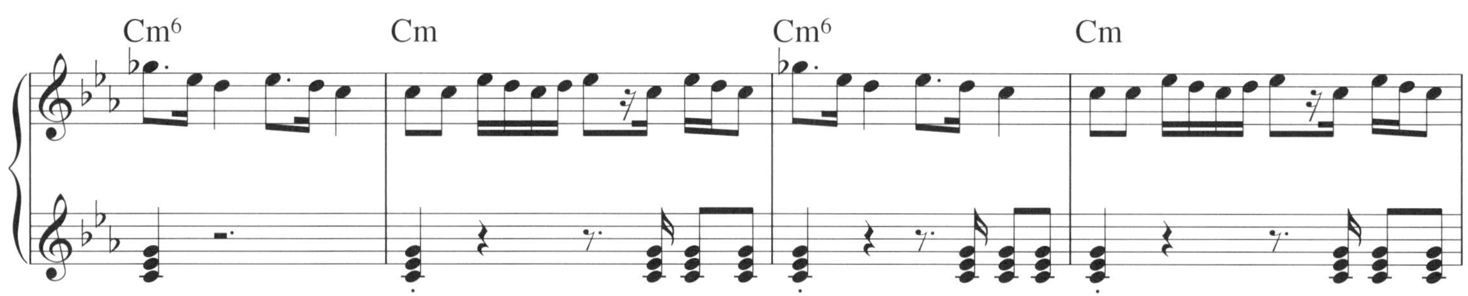

G
Cm
Cm6
I'm fall - ing.
Cm
2. There's no es - cape,
3. It's get - ting late
I can't wait.
to give you up.
I need a hit,
I took a sip
ba - by, give me it.
from my dev - il's cup.
E♭
You're dan - ge - rous,
Slow - ly,
G
Cm
Cm6
I'm lov - ing it.
it's tak - ing o - ver me.
Cm
Too high,
Too high,
can't come down.
can't come down.
Los - ing my head, spin - ning
It's in the air and it's

E♭
G
round and round.
all a - round.
Can you feel me now?
Can you feel me now?

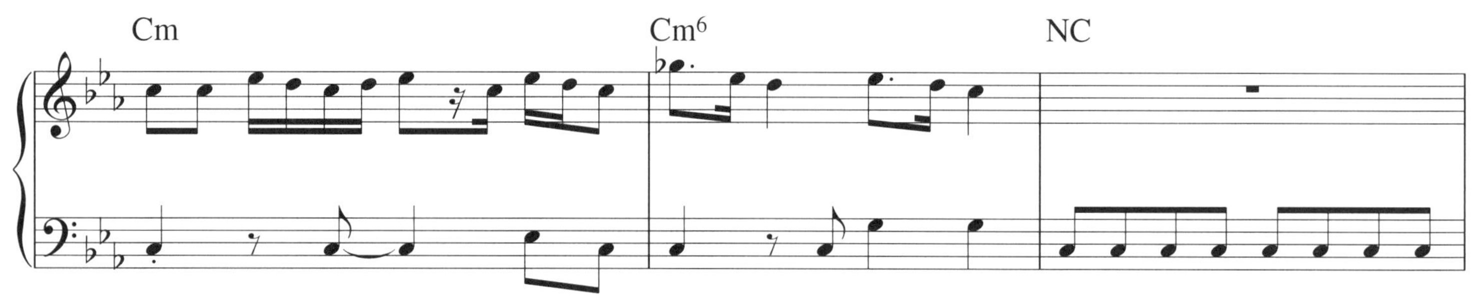
Cm
Cm6
NC

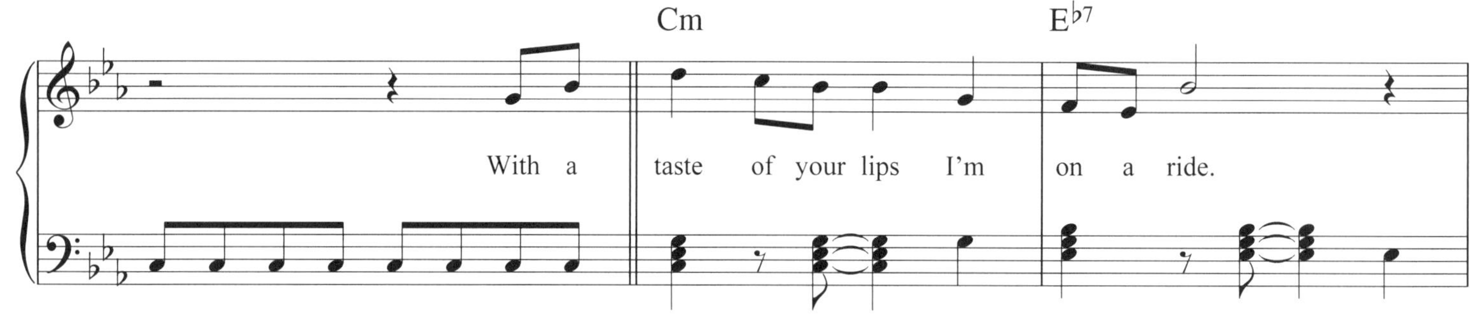
Cm
E♭7
With a
taste of your lips I'm
on a ride.

D7
D♭7
Cm
You're tox - ic
I'm slip - ping un - der.
With the
taste of a poi - son

E♭7
A♭
Gm7
D♭7
pa - ra - dise,
I'm ad - dic - ted to you. Don't you
know that you're tox - ic?

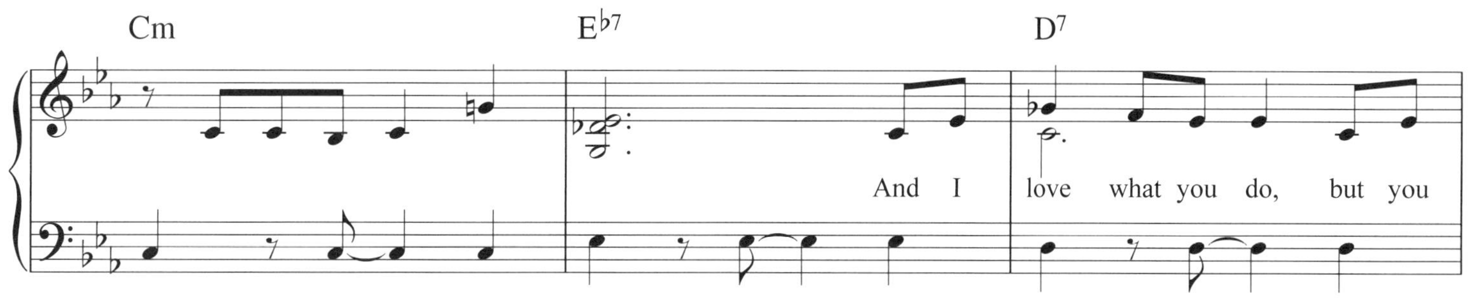
Cm
E♭7
D7
And I
love what you do, but you

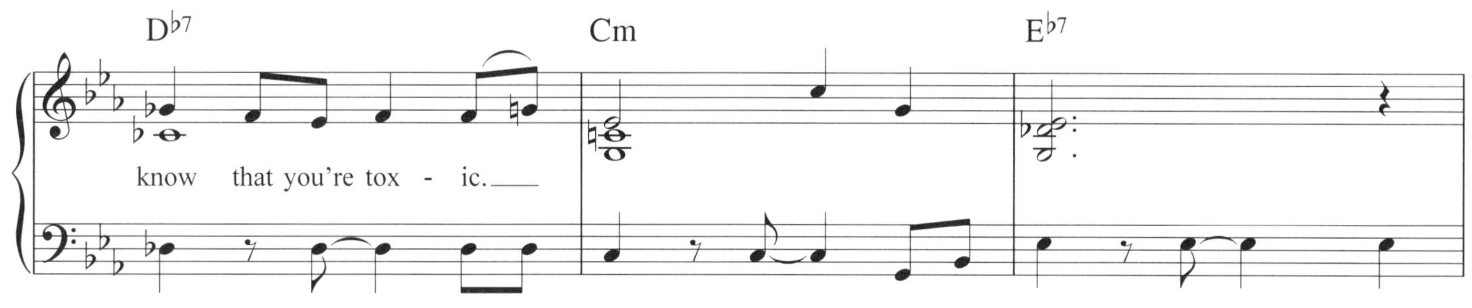
D♭7
Cm
E♭7
know that you're tox - ic.

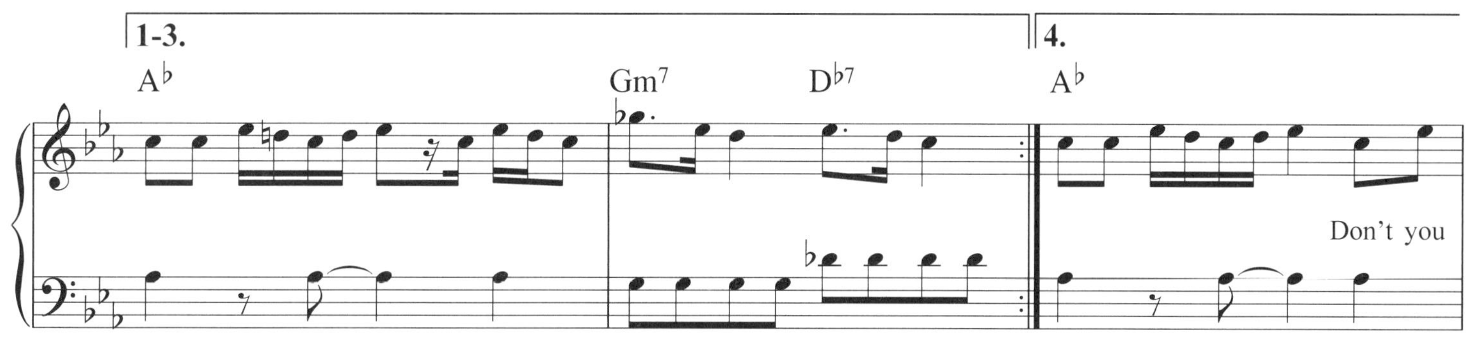
1-3.
4.
A♭
Gm7
D♭7
A♭
Don't you

Gm7
N.C.
know that you're tox - ic?
Ah,
ah,

ah.
Ah

ah
ah.

Taste of your lips I'm

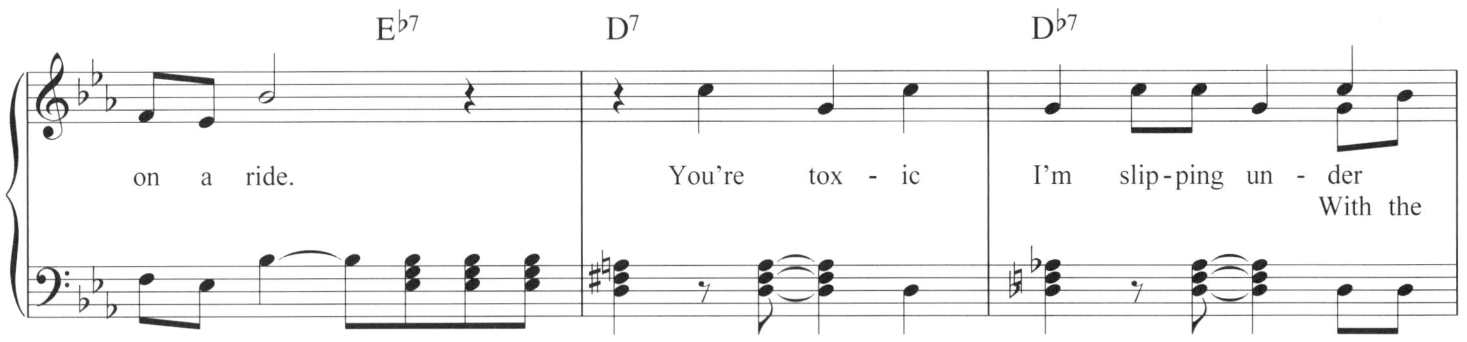
E♭7
D7
D♭7
on a ride.
You're tox - ic
I'm slip-ping un - der
With the

Cm
E♭7
A♭
taste of a poi - son
pa - ra - dise,
I'm ad - dic - ted to you.
Don't you

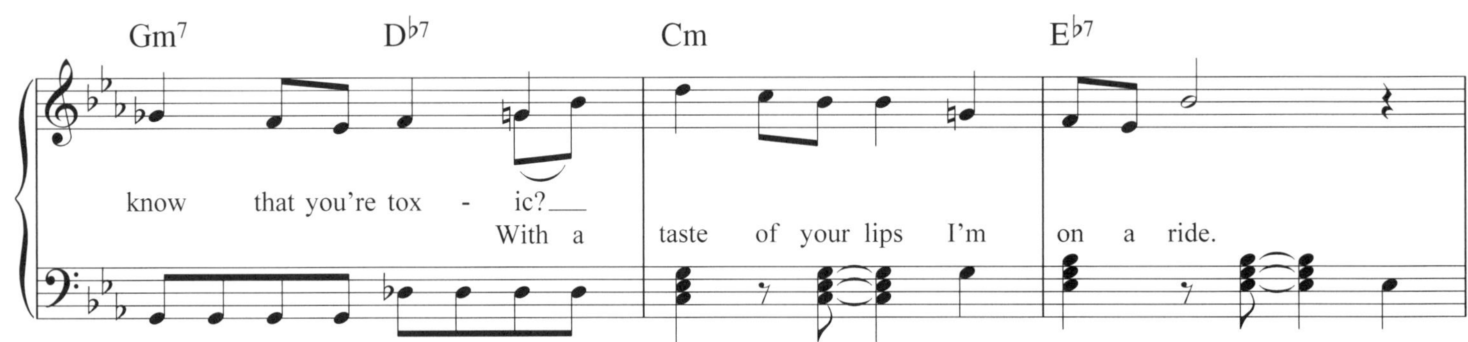
Gm7
D♭7
Cm
E♭7
know that you're tox - ic?
With a
taste of your lips I'm
on a ride.

D7
D♭7
Cm
You're tox - ic I'm slip-ping un - der.
With the taste of a poi - son

E♭7
A♭
Gm7
D♭7
pa - ra - dise, I'm ad - dic - ted to you. Don't you know that you're tox - ic?

Cm
E♭7
In - tox - i - cate me now with your lov - ing now.

D7
D♭7
Cm
I think I'm rea - dy now. (I think I'm rea - dy now.) In - tox - i - cate me now

E♭7
A♭
N.C.
with your lov - ing now. I think I'm rea - dy now.

Try A Little Tenderness

Words & Music by Harry Woods,
Jimmy Campbell & Reg Connelly

E7
Am
A7
-men - tal, she has her grief and care. And a

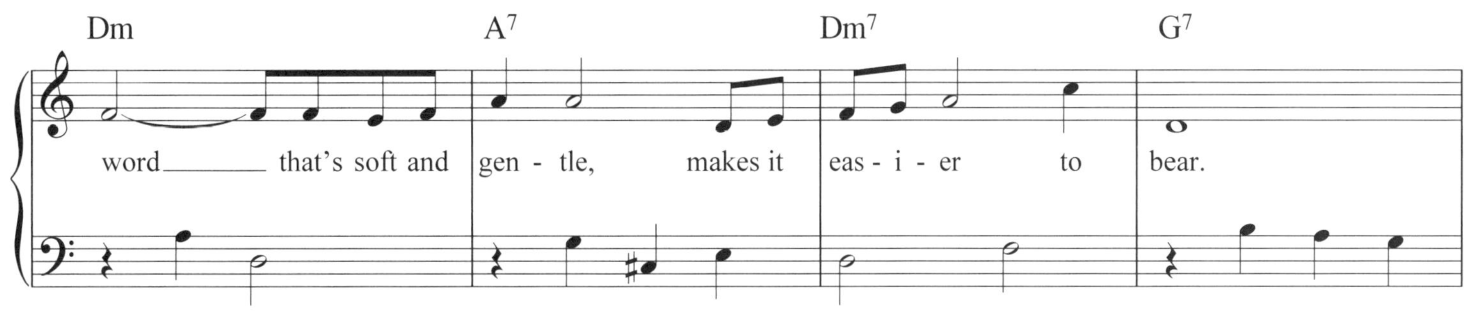
Dm
A7
Dm7
G7
word that's soft and gen - tle, makes it eas - i - er to bear.

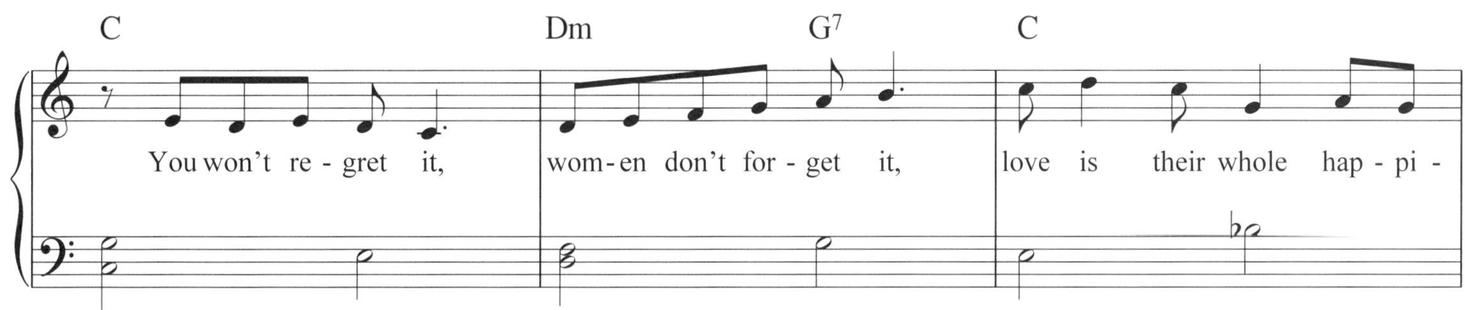
C
Dm
G7
C
You won't re - gret it, wom - en don't for - get it, love is their whole hap - pi -

A7
D7
Dm
G9
- ness. It's all so eas - y, try a lit - tle ten - der -

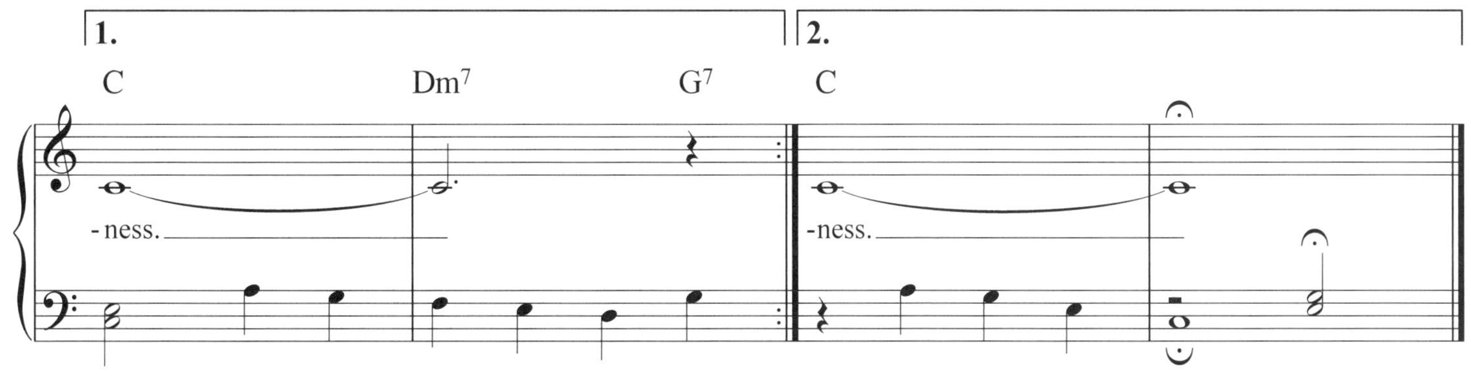
1.
2.
C
Dm7
G7
C
- ness.
- ness.

Unchained Melody

Words by Hy Zaret
Music by Alex North

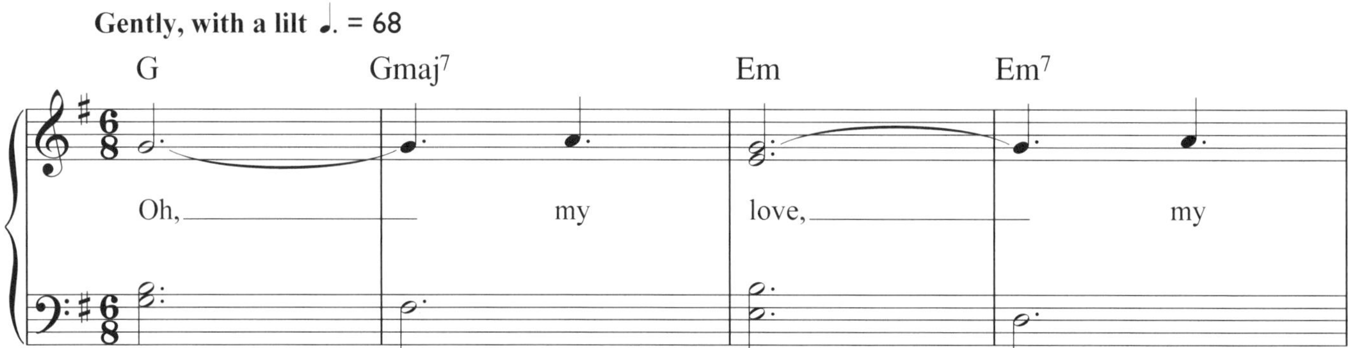

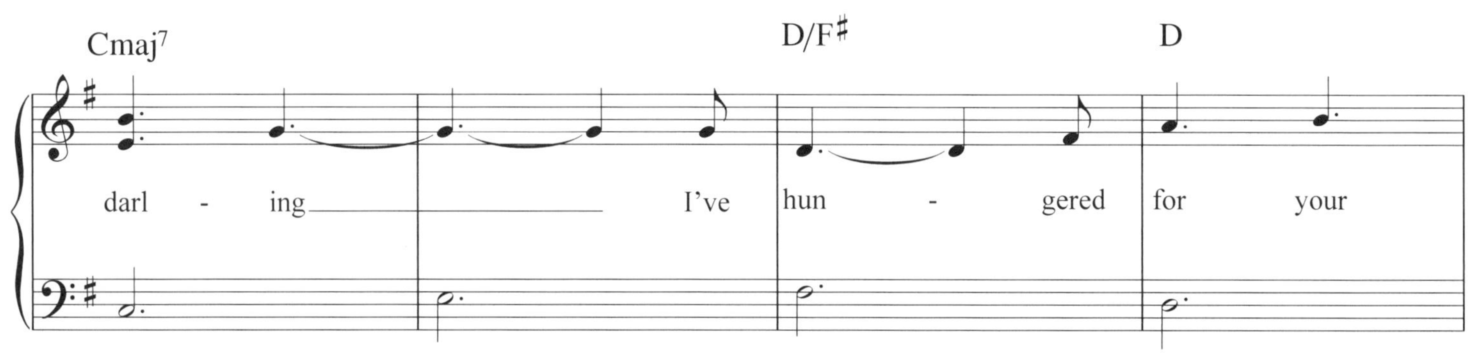

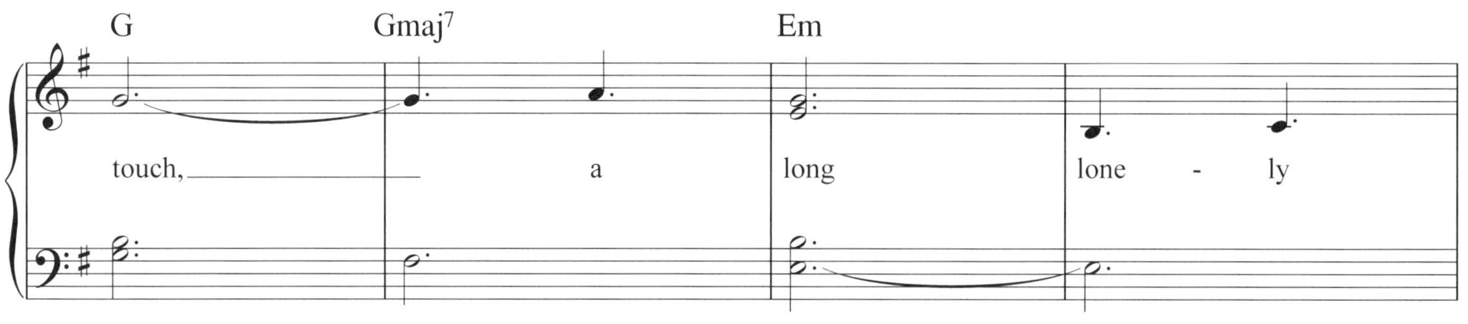

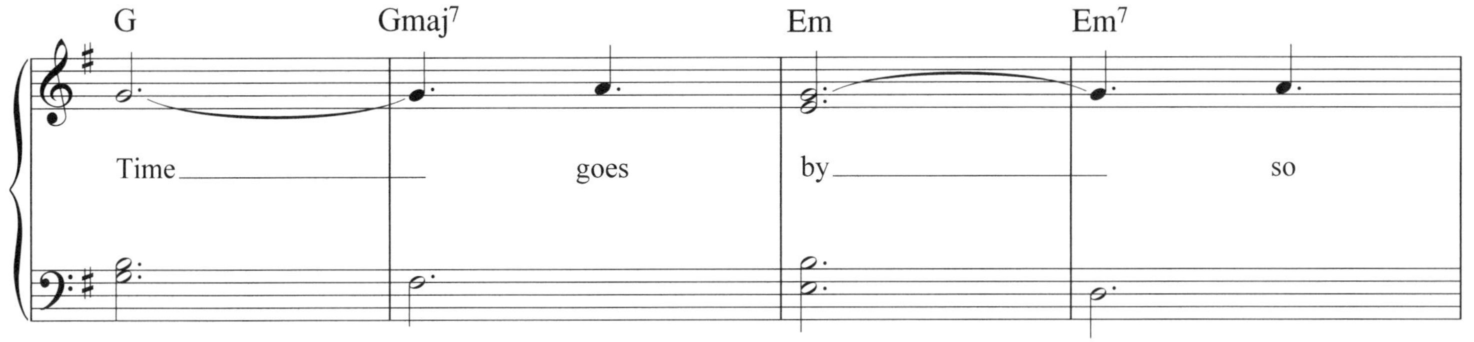
G
Gmaj7
Em
Em7
Time
goes
by
so

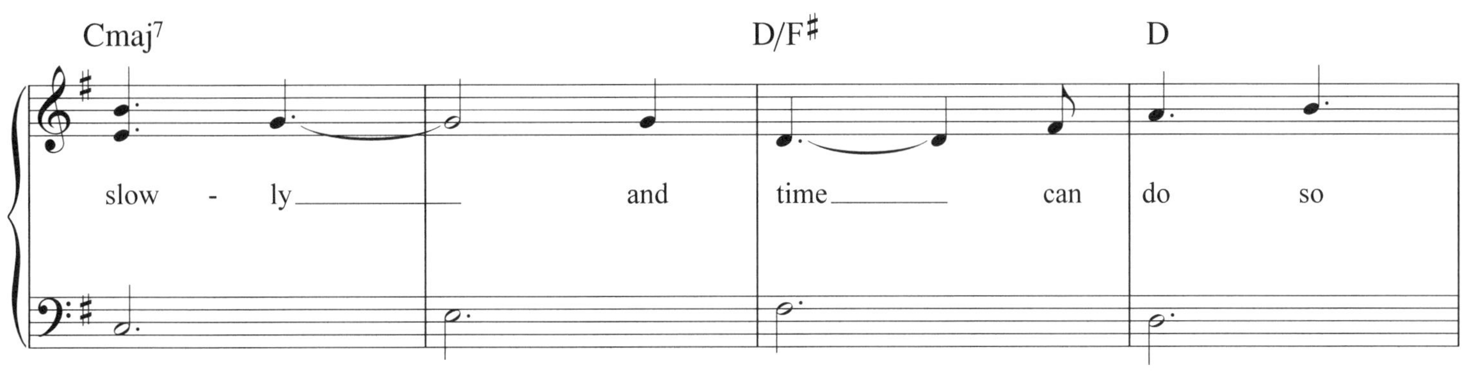
Cmaj7
D/F♯
D
slow - ly
and
time
can
do
so

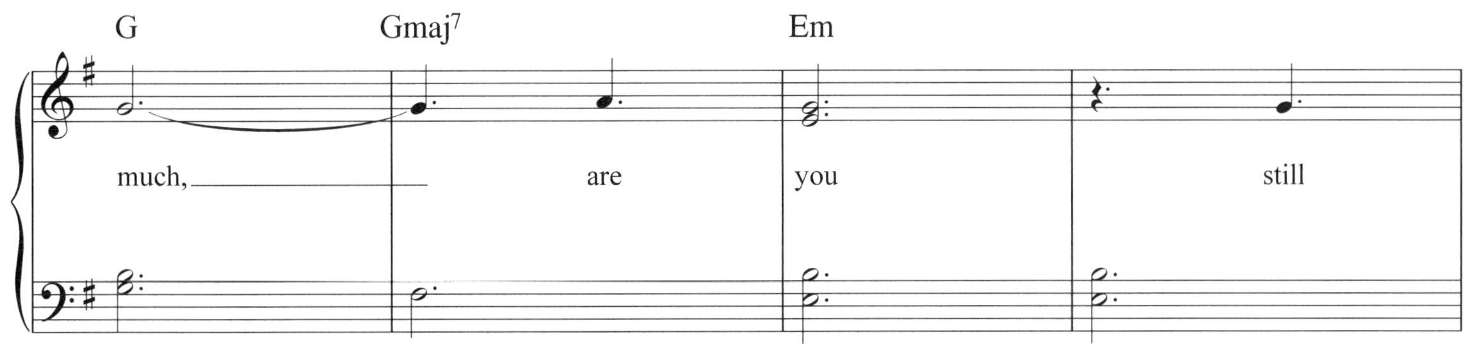
G
Gmaj7
Em
much,
are
you
still

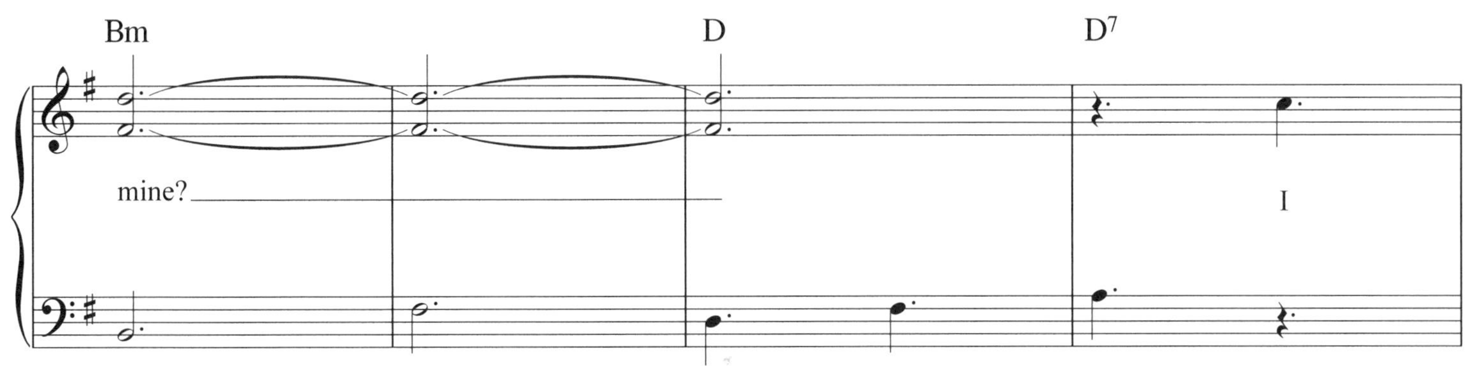
Bm
D
D7
mine?
I

G
D/F♯
need your love,
I

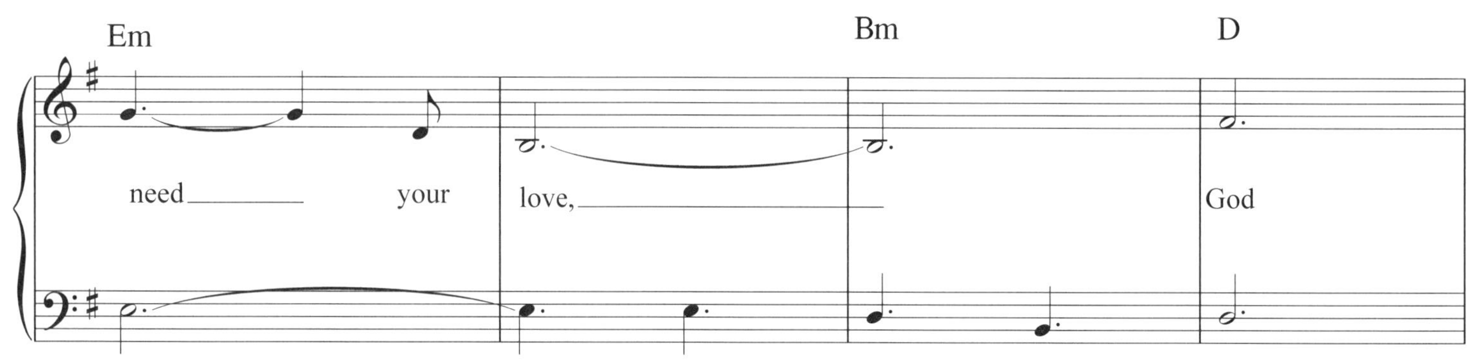
Em
Bm
D
need your love,
God

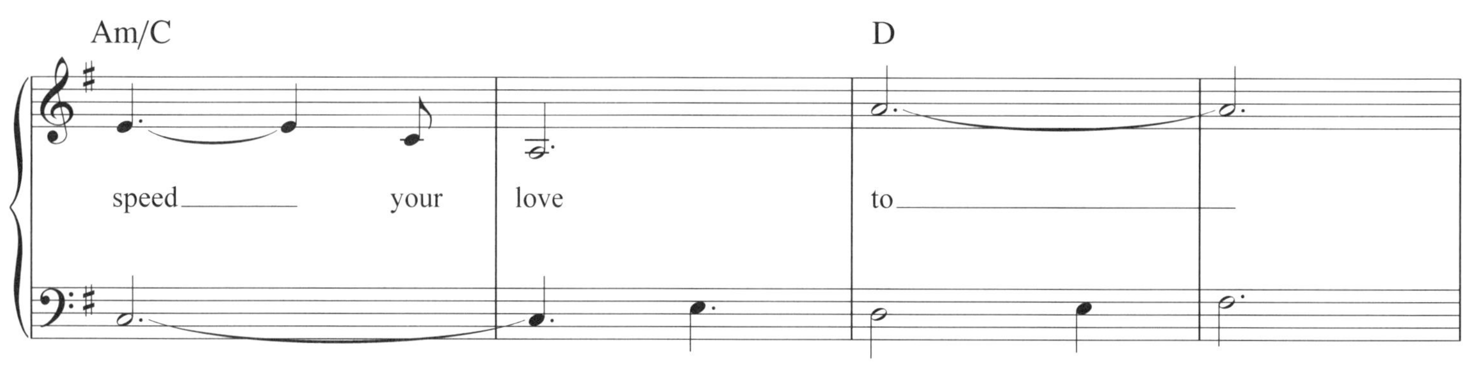
Am/C
D
speed your love
to

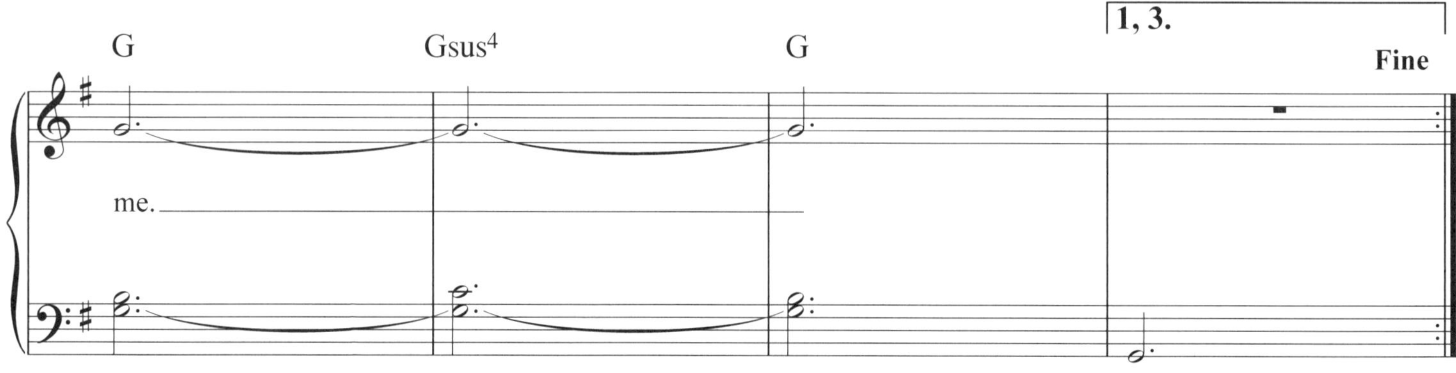
G
Gsus4
G
1, 3.
Fine
me.

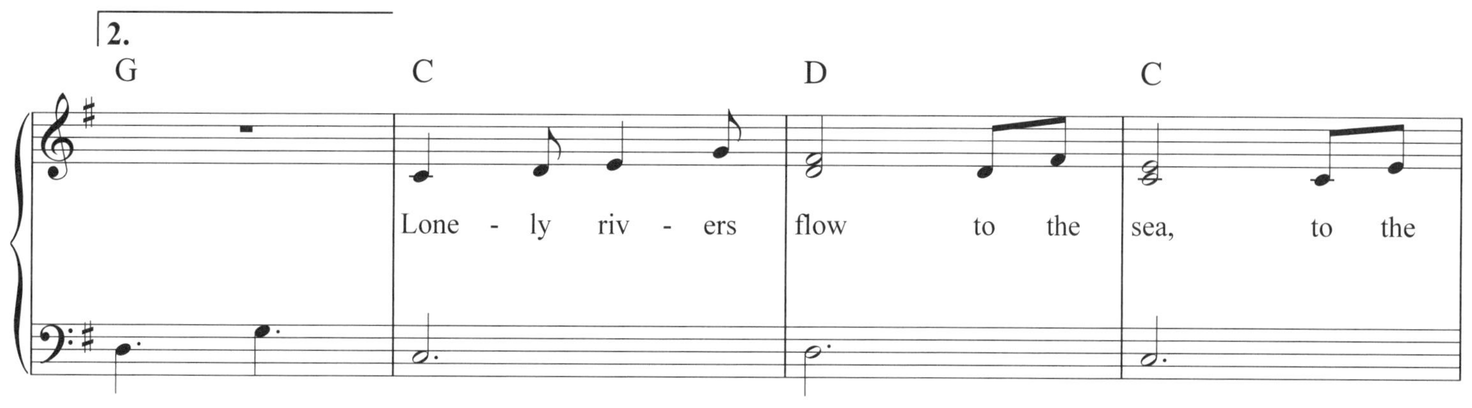
2.
G
C
D
C
Lone - ly riv - ers flow to the sea, to the

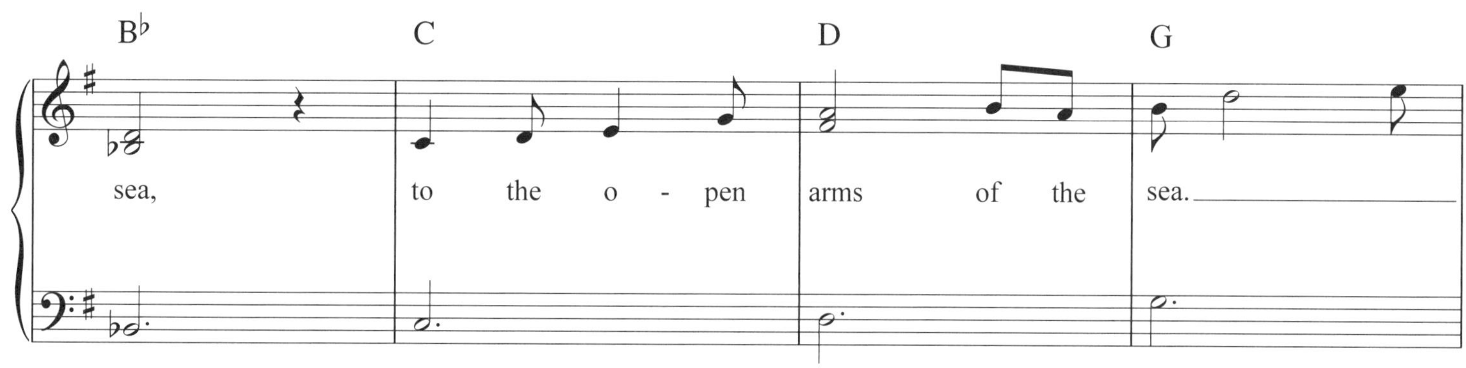
B♭
C
D
G
sea, to the o - pen arms of the sea.

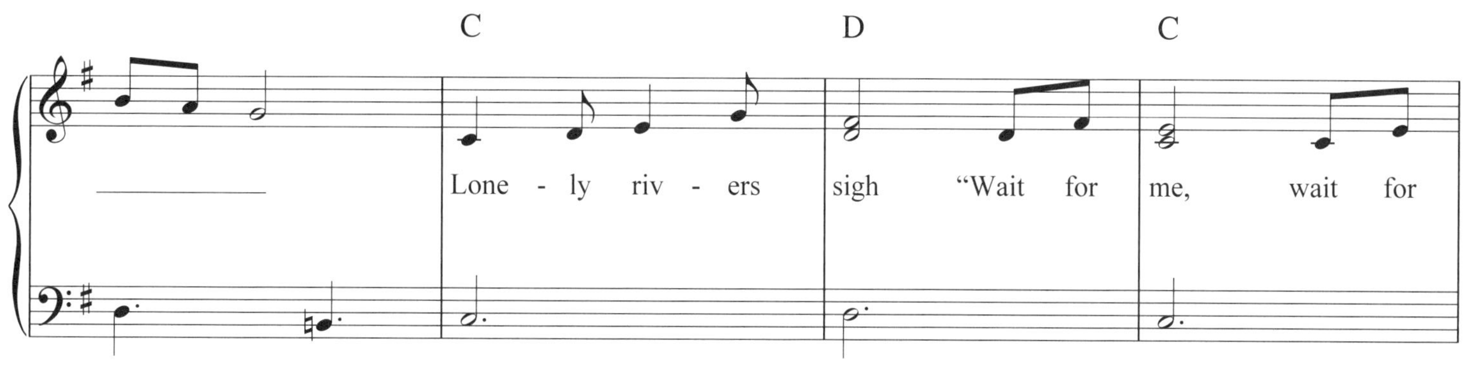
C
D
C
Lone - ly riv - ers sigh "Wait for me, wait for

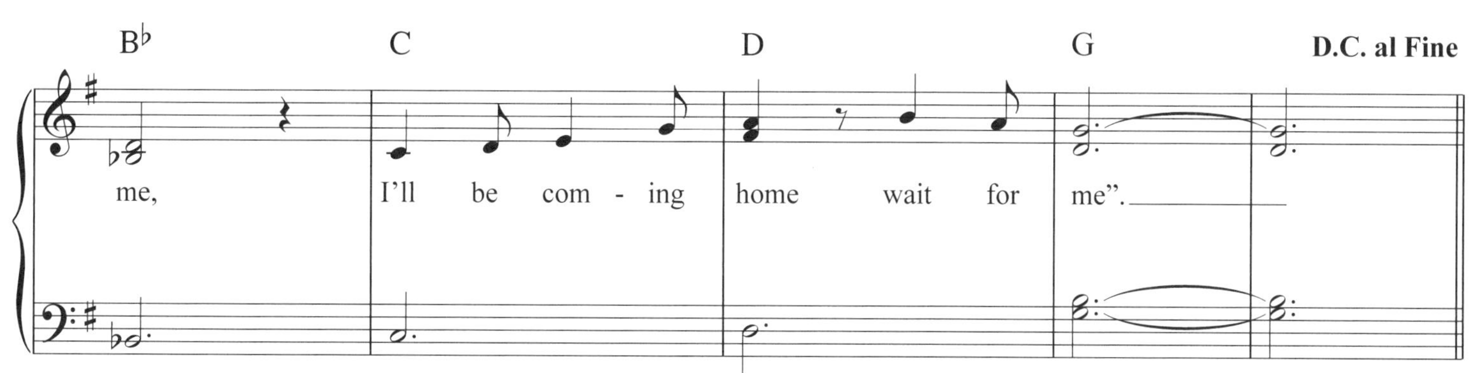
B♭
C
D
G
D.C. al Fine
me, I'll be com - ing home wait for me".

Waterloo

Words & Music by Benny Andersson,
Stig Anderson & Björn Ulvaeus

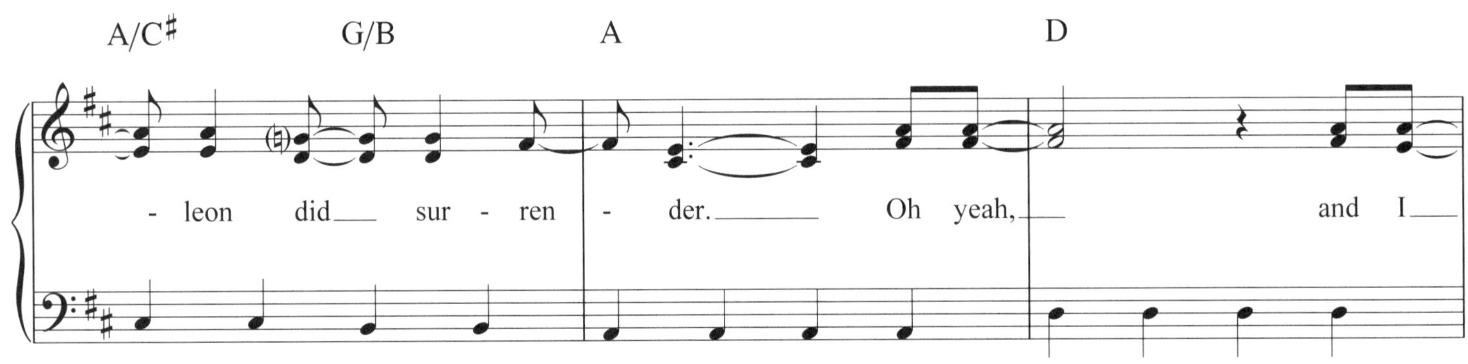

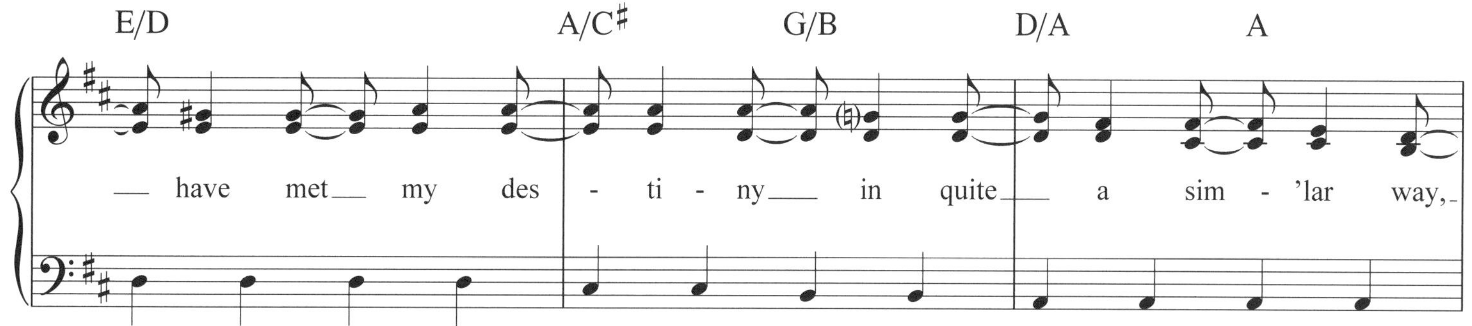
E/D
A/C♯
G/B
D/A
A
have met my des - ti - ny in quite a sim - 'lar way,

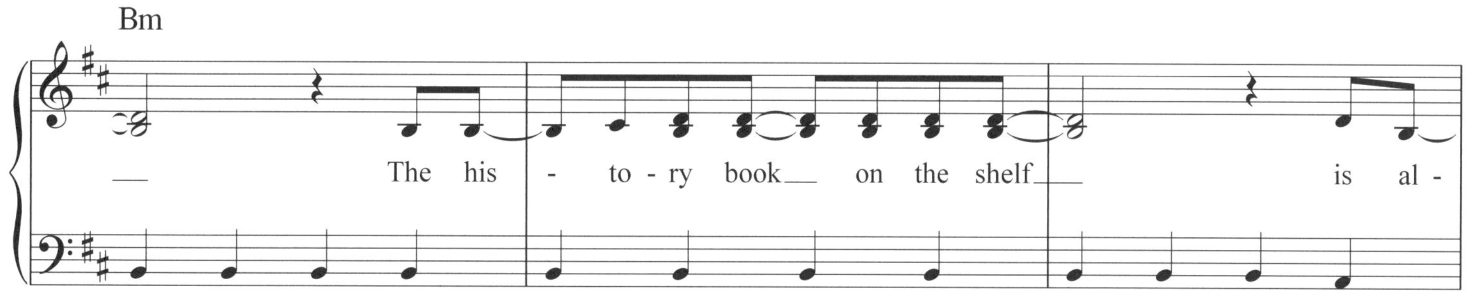
Bm
The his - to - ry book on the shelf is al -

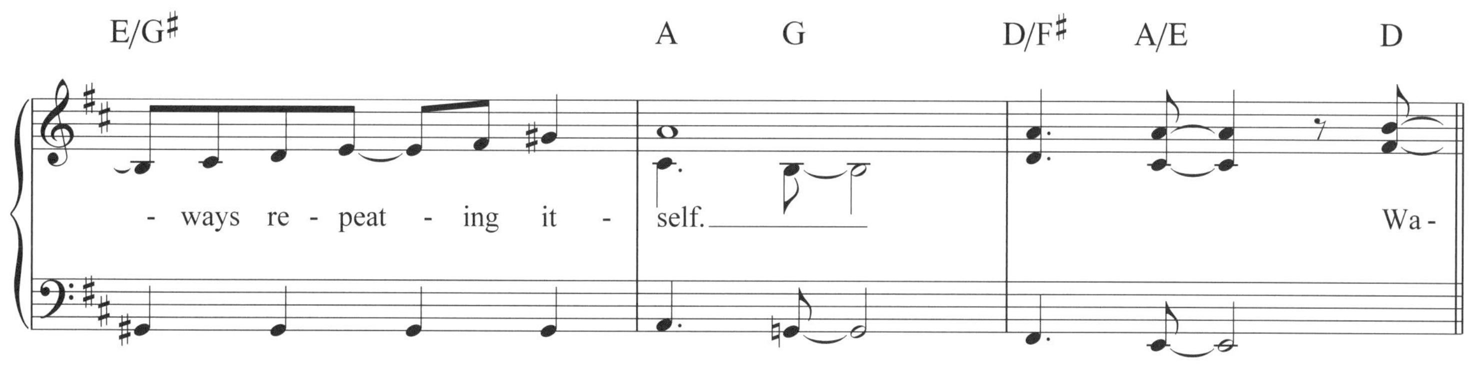
E/G♯
A
G
D/F♯
A/E
D
- ways re - peat - ing it - self.
Wa -

G
- ter - loo, I was de - feat - ed you won the war.

A
Wa - ter - loo, prom - ise to love you for ev -

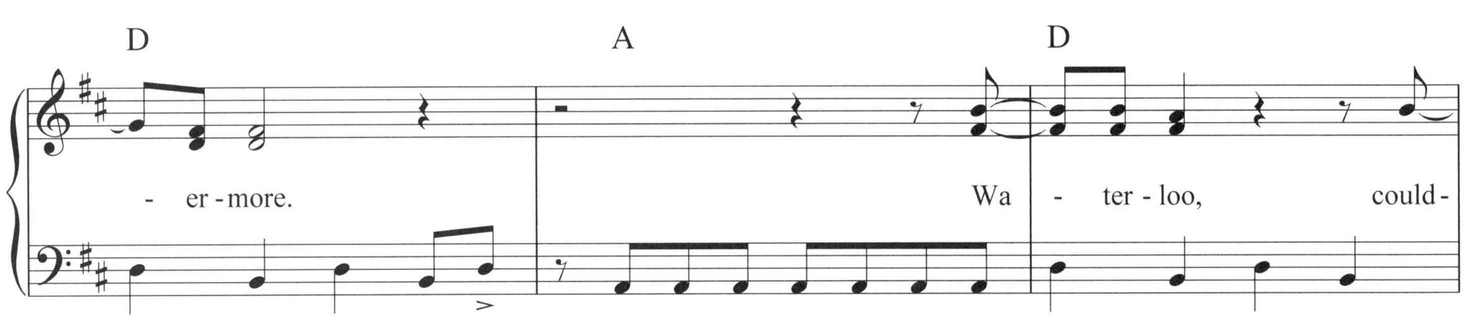
D A D
- er - more. Wa - ter - loo, could -

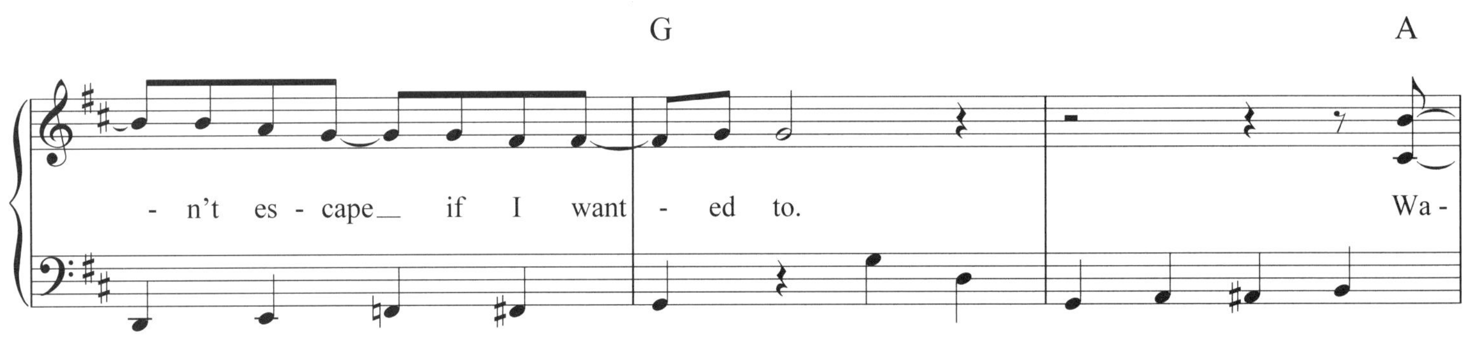
G A
- n't es - cape if I want - ed to. Wa -

D
- ter - loo, know - ing my fate is to be with you. Wa -

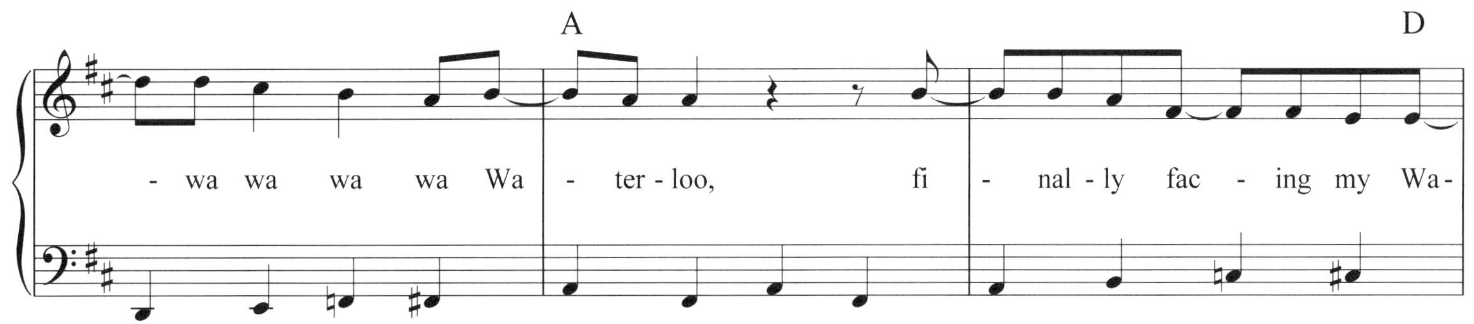
A
D
- wa wa wa wa Wa - ter - loo, fi - nal - ly fac - ing my Wa -

A
- ter - loo. Wa wa wa wa Wa - ter - loo, fi -

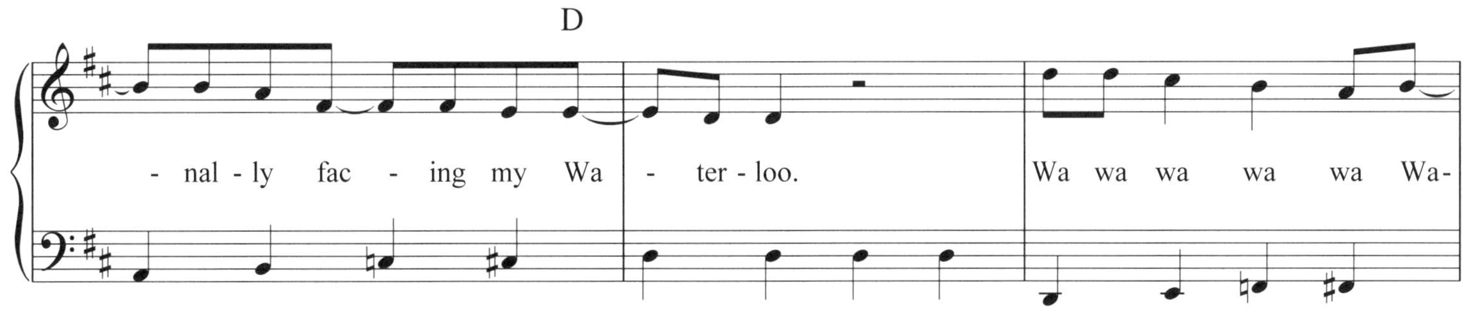
D
- nal - ly fac - ing my Wa - ter - loo. Wa wa wa wa wa Wa -

A
D
- ter - loo, fi - nal - ly fac - ing my Wa - ter - loo.

When You Say Nothing At All

Words & Music by Don Schlitz & Paul Overstreet

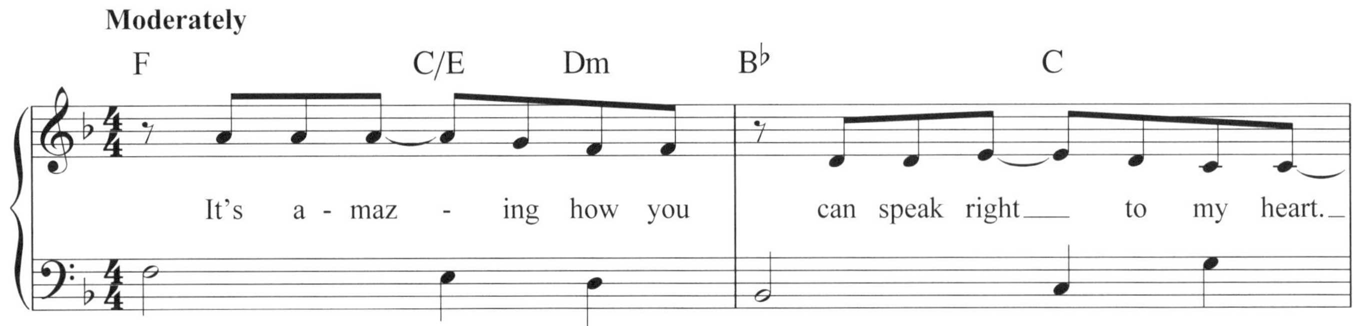

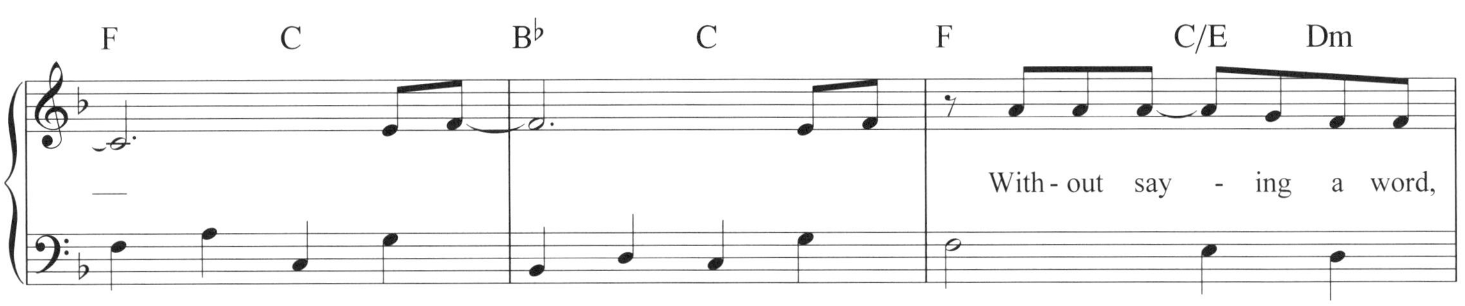

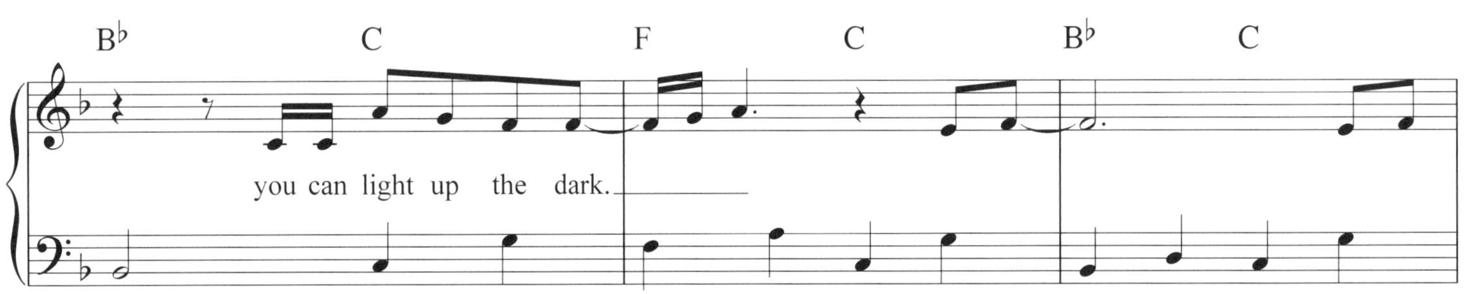

B♭ C
say a thing. The
F C/E B♭/D C
smile on your face lets me know that you need me; there's a
F C/E B♭/D C
truth in your eyes say - ing you'll nev - er leave me. The
F C/E B♭/D B♭
touch of your hand says you'll catch me wher - ev - er I fall.
C B♭ C
B♭ F/C C7 F
You say it best when you say noth - ing at all.

A Whole New World

Music by Alan Menken
Words by Tim Rice

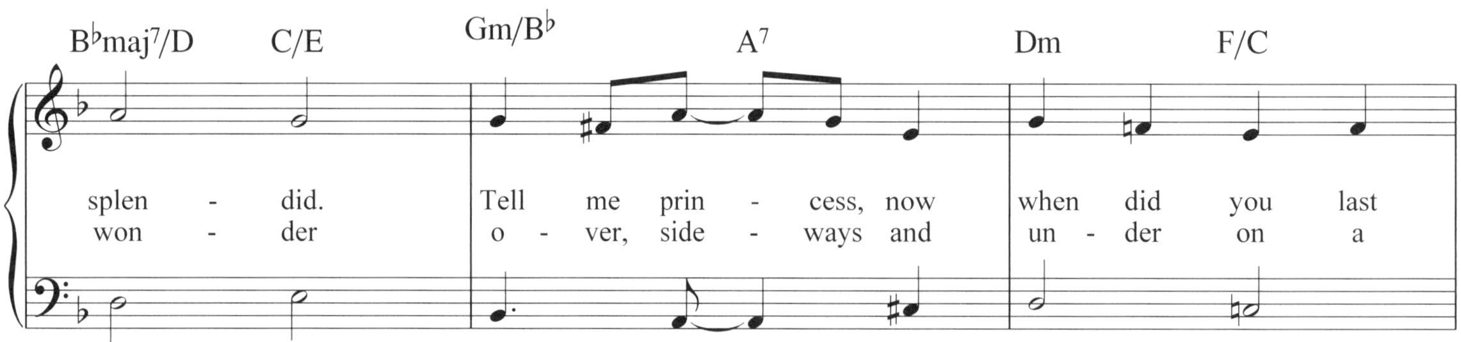

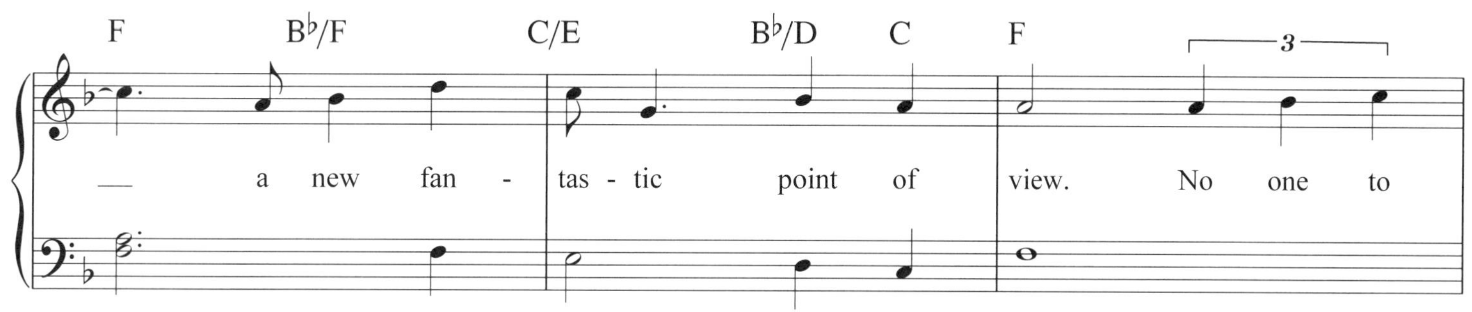
F B♭/F C/E B♭/D C F
3
— a new fan - tas - tic point of view. No one to

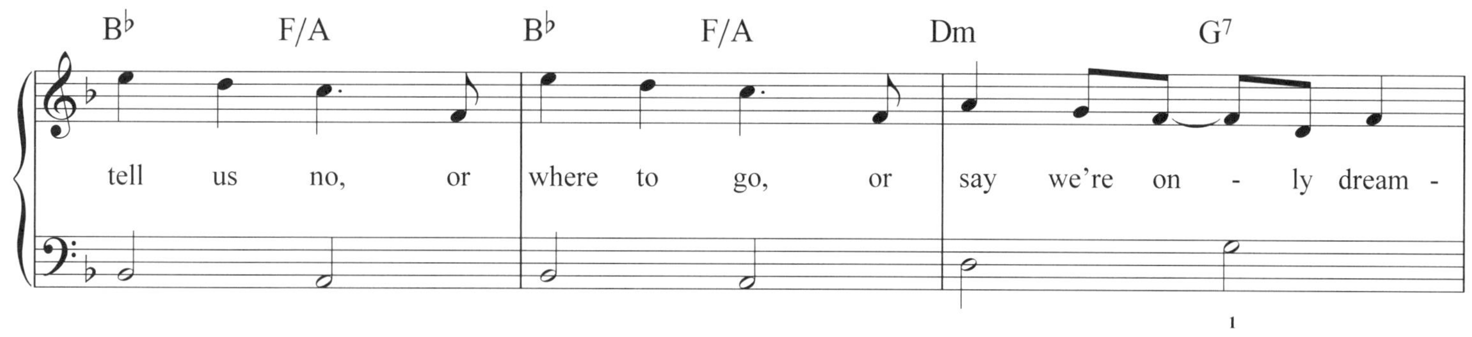
B♭ F/A B♭ F/A Dm G7
tell us no, or where to go, or say we're on - ly dream -

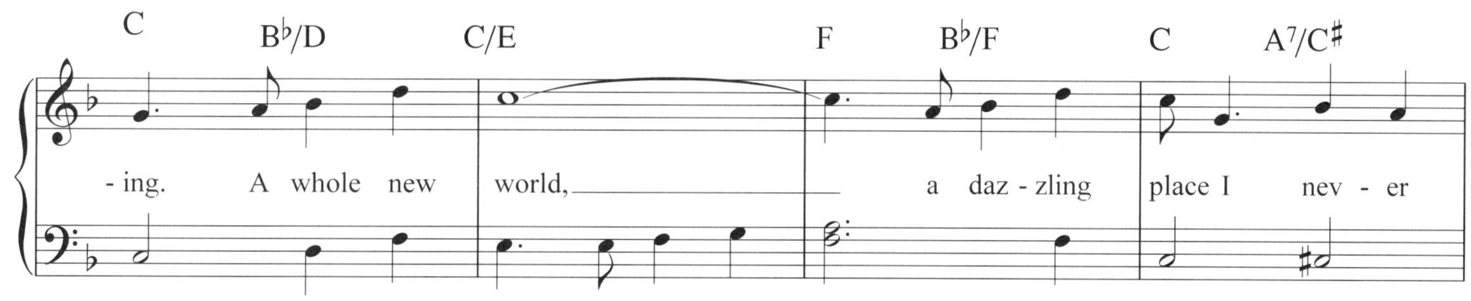
C B♭/D C/E F B♭/F C A7/C♯
- ing. A whole new world, a daz - zling place I nev - er

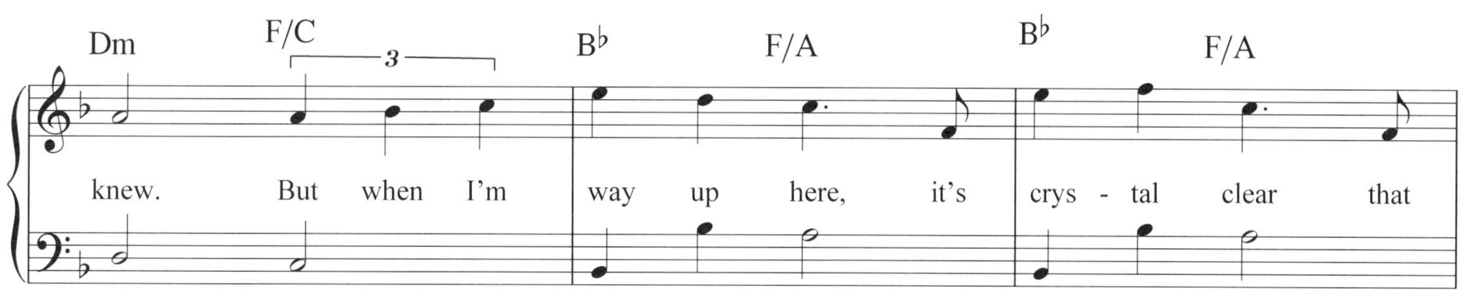
Dm F/C B♭ F/A B♭ F/A
3
knew. But when I'm way up here, it's crys - tal clear that

Dm G7 E♭ C7sus4 C7 F
now I'm in a whole new world with you.

You'll Never Walk Alone

Words by Oscar Hammerstein II
Music by Richard Rodgers

With warmth, like a hymn

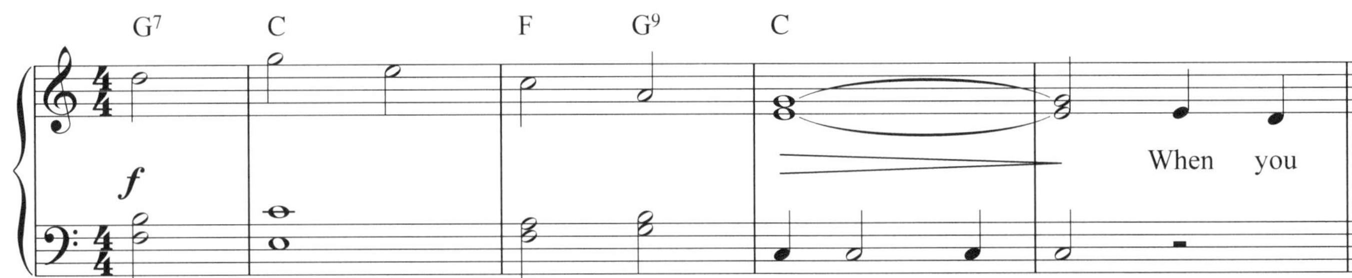

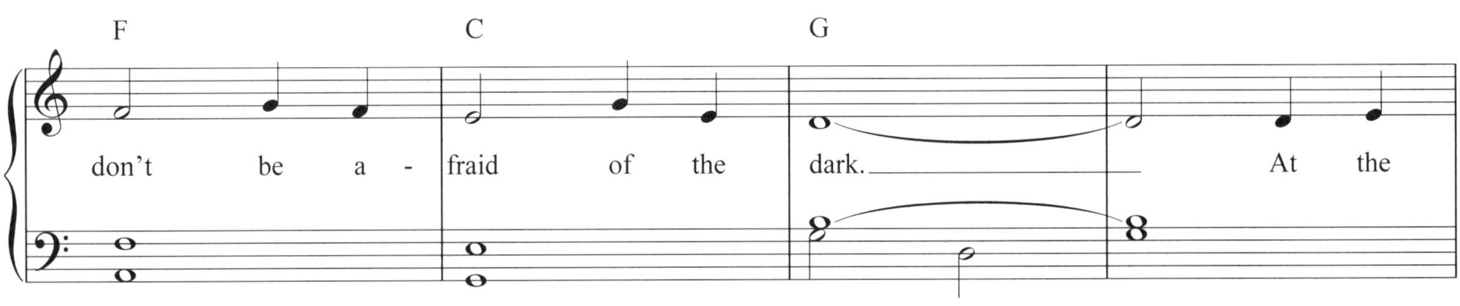

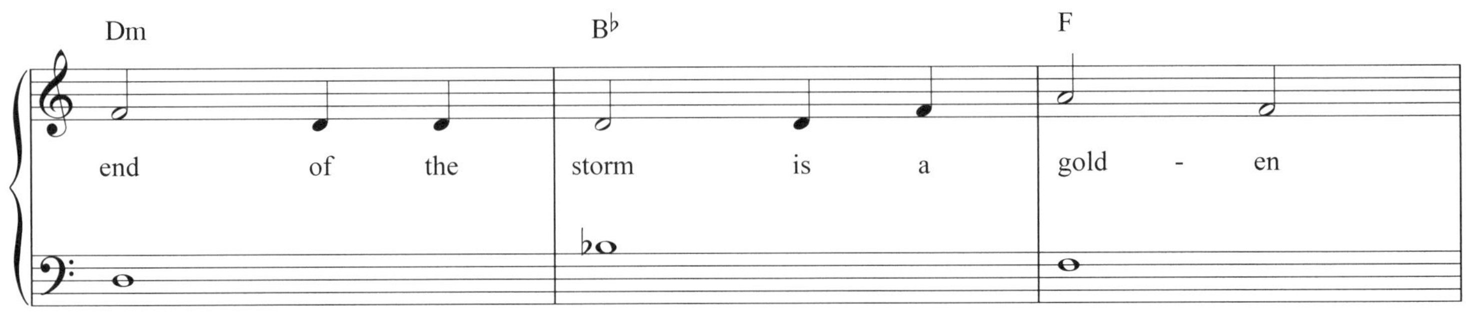

Dm
B♭
F
B♭6
F
sky and the sweet sil - ver song of a
E
C7
F
lark. Walk on through the
Fdim
C
Fm6
wind, walk on through the rain, though your
C
Am7
Dm7
dreams be tossed and blown.
G
C
Caug
Walk on, walk on, with

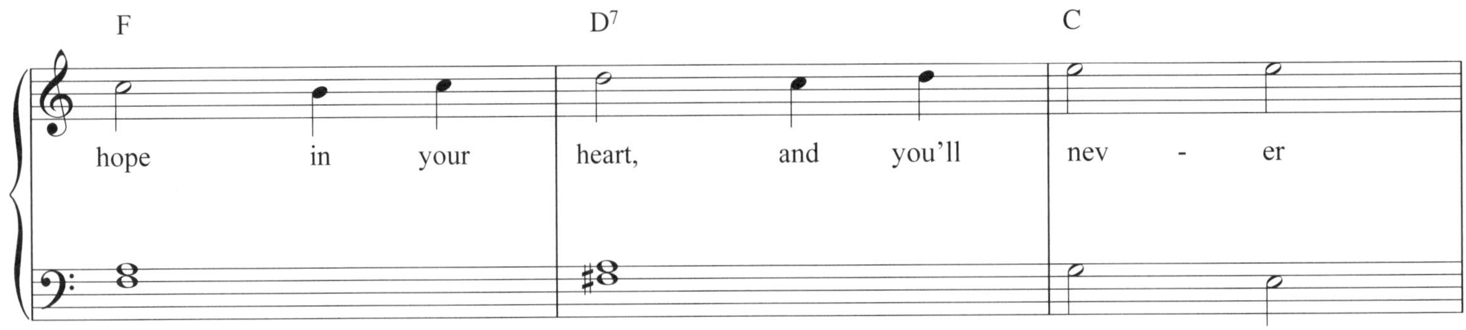
F
D7
C
hope in your
heart, and you'll
nev - er

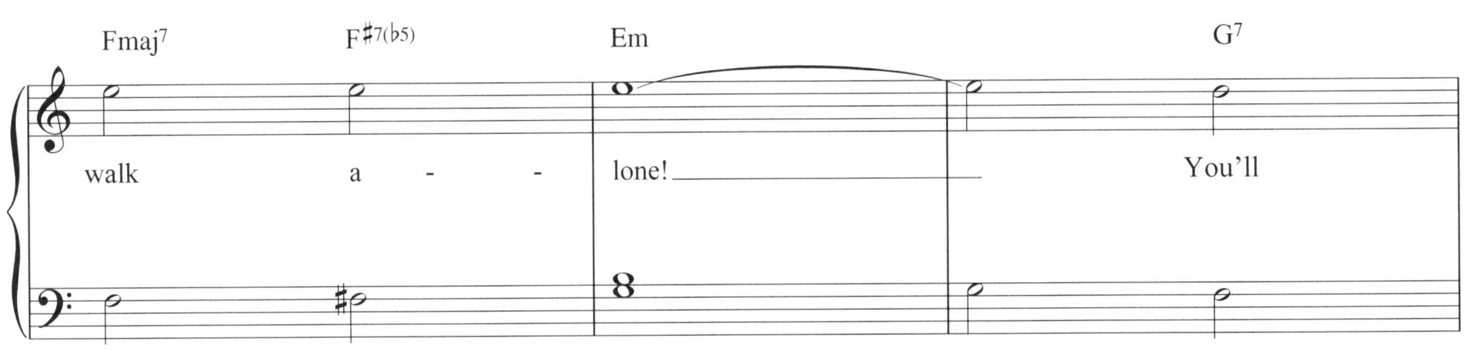
Fmaj7
F♯7(♭5)
Em
G7
walk a - -
lone!
You'll

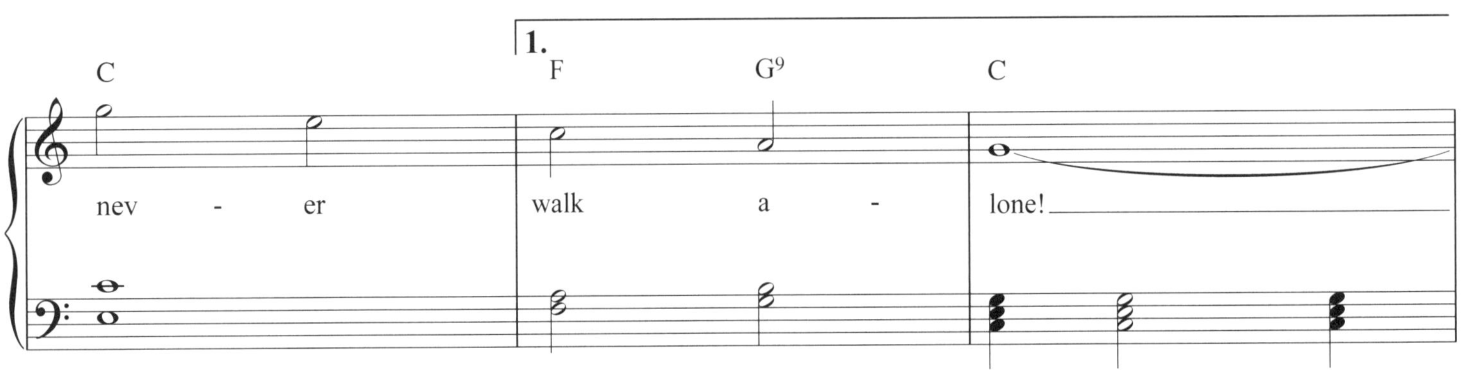
1.
C
F
G9
C
nev - er
walk a -
lone!

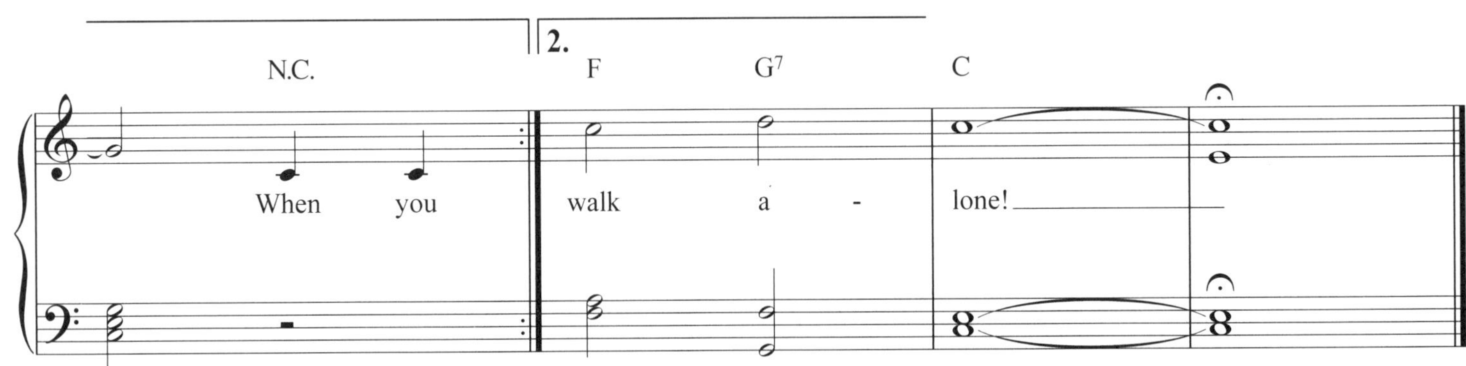
2.
N.C.
F
G7
C
When you
walk a -
lone!

3 4 5 6 7 8